Pain: A Love Story

Pain: A Love Story

Serena Sterling, MA, PsyD

SUMMIT PRESS
PUBLISHERS

Printed in the United States of America
First Printing, 2020
ISBN: 978-0-9863309-5-7
Library of Congress Control Number: 2020924489
Summit Press
Summit Press Publishers
411 Walnut Street # 12515
Green Cove Springs, FL 32043-3443
author@summit-success.com

Book Layout © Unauthorized Media, LLC

Quantity sales. Special discounts are available on quantity purchases by corporations, associations, and others. For details, contact author@summit-success.com

DEDICATION

DEDICATED TO THOSE WHO THINK they are unlovable, those who think there is something wrong with them, and those who think they are not good enough.

You are lovable, there is nothing wrong with you, and you are good enough.

Table of Contents

"You own everything that happened to you.

Tell your stories.

If people wanted you to write warmly about them, they should have behaved better."

—*Anne Lamott*

"She needed someone
to heal her,

so she became
a healer."

—*Alex Myles*

PREFACE

THREE WEEKS INTO MY DREAM job as assistant editor at Spirituality & Health magazine and I'm agitated—the subway is crawling, and I'm going to be late. Some guy rubs up against me, but I figure this is New York City; it's part of the experience.

Finally, we arrive at my stop, Wall Street Station, but we just sit there. The doors remain closed, the engine shuts off, and smoke fills the train. We're told to head toward the rear.

As we do, the doors open.

When we finally reach the street, I can see no more than five feet in front of me. Normally, I can see all the way to the end of the block and beyond. But that day, everything is gray; papers swirl past me, my feet are covered in ash, and smoke fills my lungs.

Out of nowhere, FBI agents in gas masks appear and yell, "Run ... run for your life ... RUN!"

There are any number of versions of the 9/11 story. This one just happens to be mine. But it's just part of my story.

In the weeks that follow, I become progressively tired and stiff; I'm in constant pain, even more so than usual. Sleep feels better than being awake. I lose my drive, focus, and motivation—I risk losing everything I worked so hard to gain. When my boss tells me to do something, I need him to repeat it multiple times just to remember it. A few more weeks of this and I'd be out of a job.

I go to my medical doctor and he tells me I have chronic fatigue syndrome. "There's no cure, you'll have to learn to cope with it."

Having dealt with chronic pain since I was nine years old, the idea of living with debilitating fatigue and joint pain for the rest of my life is beyond depressing.

I decide to find a doctor who can really help me. I've been to a million doctors before. Most were ineffectual or made me feel far worse, so I recognize it will be no easy task.

I find one, but she does woo-woo, out-there stuff. Thanks to juvenile rheumatoid arthritis, I've been seeing chiropractors for over a decade; she's different. She does hand mudras: she presses on my arm and it changes from weak to strong, depending on the question. "Helpless," she says, and my arm goes weak. She tells me to explain how I felt helpless on 9/11.

"Look lady, I think most people felt helpless on 9/11."

She encourages me to tell her anyway. Then she presses my arm again and starts counting, from birth to ten, ten to twenty, ten to fifteen. "Ten, eleven, twelve, thirteen, fourteen." She stops pressing when she has some sort of answer. "OK, what happened at fourteen where you felt helpless?" she asks.

And just like that, a flood of tears wells up and pours down my face—something rare for me, because I'm very good at holding everything in, never showing weakness.

I remember my best friend telling me, "I don't want to be

friends with you anymore. You suck!" Then she turned all our friends against me, leaving me helpless to change their minds.

For the first time in my life, my grades plummeted. I always got A's and B's and now I was getting C's and even a few D's. My ambitious parents were furious. "Colleges start looking at transcripts beginning in ninth grade, so get your act together!" Since I wasn't close to them, I bottled it all up—just like I bottled up my feeling of helplessness on 9/11.

Dr. Linda Randazzo, with her weird techniques, was able to find the emotions I had buried on 9/11. She found helplessness and a whole bunch of other feelings I wasn't even aware I felt that day and didn't express.

Once I identify and express how I felt negative emotions "back then," I don't have to feel them anymore.

I feel lighter. I have more clarity. I have more energy and the achiness in my joints goes away. I walk home after my appointment. I walk three miles—this after not being able to walk more than three blocks without feeling fatigued. I'm intrigued. I continue seeing her.

Dr. Randazzo gets me all better in three weeks. Three weeks! I don't have to learn to cope with debilitating fatigue for the rest of my life or take medications.

That healing experience changes everything for me. It is the inciting incident that launches me on the journey to not only heal myself, but others. It drives home the fact that our mental health affects our physical health, and what happens to our bodies affects our mental and emotional well-being. The cycle is inexorably linked. Suddenly, my journalism career matters not one whit, and I want nothing more than to learn how to do for others what Dr. Randazzo did for me.

Like many experts who had to learn to help themselves first, I began helping others identify stuck emotions so they too could take action to solve their own chronic pain issues, be they physical or emotional. I help them understand how their thoughts and beliefs affect their bodies; how their relationships harm or heal them; how their reactions to the people in their lives, and the way they repress or express their emotion, influence their health, create their experiences and their chronic pain. Their stories, and how they interpret them, are what create their perceptions and their realities, their pain. The whole goal is to get at those stories, which are usually buried six feet deep. Examples of such stories I share herein.

But it's not enough to understand that trapped emotions create illness of some form in the body. We must also understand how that dynamic sets up, not just in clinical terms, but in day-to-day interactions. When we look at life with these lenses, we have a better shot at addressing our pain. And that starts with understanding that we humans store emotions in our body for a whole host of reasons, and they need to be released or we'll continue to be in pain. We need to better cope with the never-ending stream of stressors that come our way because there's no escape.

There are various ways of identifying stuck emotions and reasons for why we feel a certain way and why things aren't working in our lives. Physical symptoms are often a communication tool our bodies use to signal that something is off. A backache is not always due to some structural issue. When the pain doesn't improve after taking medications, applying physical therapy techniques, having chiropractic adjustments, or doing some other intervention, there may be some mental or emotional stress getting stuck in the body.

I wrote this book for people considering that possibility.

. . . for those with chronic pain and functional disorders,

whose diagnostic tests are normal but who don't feel well and are in a level of pain that has lowered their quality of life. Psychosomatic conditions sum up the type of issues I address, but most people don't like that word because it makes it sound like it's all in their mind and they made up their pain.

. . . for those who have been diagnosed as having Tension Myositis Syndrome, Psychophysiologic Disorders, Stress Illness, or Psychogenic Disorders. Even though each diagnosis is slightly different than the other, when it comes down to it, they're all about physical pain with an etiology based in emotional issues.

. . . for those who have been to multiple doctors or other healing practitioners, but haven't found relief. The professionals have told them that they can't find anything wrong, they can't help them, or they offer a dozen medications or surgery. Perhaps they tried these routes only to find they're no better than before, not really.

. . . for those who are tired of going to doctors time and time again only to feel more frustrated because they don't feel any different. They've tried the diets and supplements. They've talked to therapists. Yet they don't feel that examining how their families or parents treated them when they were young helps them feel different now. Talking about it, they conclude, doesn't do anything to make it any easier to live with the pain. At some point in their therapy, they got to feeling like they were talking to a friend who was good at listening; yet all that talking did not provide results. It didn't change how they were feeling or what they could do about their circumstances. The pain was still there.

Emotionally, they often feel more depressed and anxious about their issue because they wonder if anyone can really help them. Financially, they've already poured money into finding the solution. Physically, their issue is exacerbated due to the other stresses. Spiritually, they begin to lose their spark and joy and their purpose gets muddled. In other words, they feel hopeless, like a hot mess. They become more isolated and more depressed and anxious, thereby creating a vicious cycle.

Most of the people who come to me have anxiety about their career or their relationships. Some suffer from panic attacks. They suffer from chronic pain and they're desperate to feel better. They feel stuck and want to feel more at ease. They've tried the medication, the surgery, to no avail so they're looking for natural relief.

Most have wanted to move up in their careers but find that their pain holds them back. If they have jobs that require physical labor—being a server or bartender, for instance—they eventually have to quit and find some other work.

I've helped personal trainers, entrepreneurs, and corporate types. They're all good at what they do, but they know, if they just get this issue solved, they could be that much more successful. They have goals—both professional and relational—but find it easy to get bogged down in their day-to-day and lose sight of their goals. They may have had to find other friends because the ones they used to have were connected to their life when they were more physically active. Being depressed or anxious also caused some friends to leave their circle.

They realize, or are at least open to the idea, that emotions play a part in maintaining their pain—that there's something to this stress-illness/stress-pain connection they've heard about.

But here's the missing piece, their pain will never go away until they've addressed the underlying cause. That is what I hone in on.

I've helped scores of clients find relief from psychogenic chronic pain—pain that originates from a mental or emotional issue—but I'm going to let you in on a little secret: I haven't completely solved my own pain problem; I haven't healed myself of self-induced juvenile rheumatoid arthritis (though I've developed tools to get myself out of pain when it arises). But man, can I expound upon the mind/body connection when it comes to chronic pain. If anybody has wanted and needed to understand this stuff, it's me.

I wrote this book because rarely do you get to see someone with a higher degree in psychology, who has dealt with chronic pain and not fully healed themself. Most books out there are from doctors or health coaches or someone that comes from a place of "I got rid of my pain doing this method, so do this method and you'll get better, too." What I know is that there are hundreds of methods out there.

You will not find any scientific studies in this book. This is my personal story of how I ended up with physical pain, how I've learned to get relief, and how I've helped others with pain that is not alleviated by conventional methods. Will this work for everyone? No. Is there a one-size-fits-all solution to every problem? Of course not. I have found relief for myself and my clients by employing the methodologies I've learned.

Healing doesn't always happen in a seven-step process like many experts suggest. Finding the solution often takes much longer. I can certainly speak to that. For some of my clients, I can find the cause of their pain, the underlying story beneath it, in one session, and they fully recover in a few more; for others (including me), it takes more time. Some issues take a few weeks to resolve, others take a few months. If healing takes time for you, you're not an anomaly—you're not doing something wrong; you're not a failure. If that's the only takeaway you get from this book, I've done my job.

You'll find I don't label my pain. I don't call it Tension Myositis Syndrome, psychophysiologic disorder, stress illness, or anything else. It's simply pain that resulted from repressing feelings I didn't feel comfortable expressing. Remember, painful symptoms were around long before certain doctors developed their own diagnoses.

Lastly, there are certain traits most of my clients have in common with me, and they are at the heart of repression and its byproduct, pain. Perhaps you recognize them in your own life, as well . . .

- You do a lot more for others than others do for you.
- You don't put yourself first.
- You don't want to be a burden to your loved ones by complaining about your issues.
- You have a hard time relaxing and feel as though you're on a constant treadmill.
- You don't share your honest feelings about how your relationships affect you.
- You never feel good enough.
- You don't feel you're doing enough with your career, relationships, or life in general.
- You want connection, more than anything—connection to yourself and to others; you want the sense you are loved.

Imagine what would happen to your pain if you felt genuinely loved—if you felt you could speak your mind and be heard, be yourself and still be liked, drop the armor and be vulnerable, and stop trying so hard? What would it take for you to stop repressing your emotions, stuffing them deep, so you don't rock the boat, so you could heal yourself?

A rheumatologist I used to see when I was young recounted a story he'd heard of a woman who fell in love and her arthritis went away. Anecdotal evidence for sure, but I mean to explore that with you in this book, too. I want to talk about love, what it's like to be heard and seen because I've got a theory: love can heal your pain.

Despite my own misgivings, I want to share with you, not just my professional experience with chronic pain, but also my personal experience with its principal source—the human need for acceptance and love.

Many emotions end up in the unconscious because they're not acceptable to feel consciously. It's not always acceptable to feel anger and sadness and hopelessness, and so we push those feelings down and away so we don't have to deal with them or inflict them on others. If we want to be loved, we best not express those things; that's the story we've bought into. Over time, if those feelings don't get expressed in one way or another, they'll come out sideways. They'll take the form of any number of symptoms, like pain, anxiety, depression, fatigue, always being sick or injured, difficulty recovering, and the list goes on.

Whether it's grief, shame, anger, or resentment, these are emotions that are not always easy to share with others, or even ourselves, so we walk around as if they don't bother us when they do. When they're not expressed, they often come out in the form of mental, emotional, and physical symptoms.

Once you look at what might be causing a symptom, even acknowledge it, then you can release it.

These symptoms are often a distraction, allowing you to avoid emotional pain. Your body is not betraying you by afflicting you with pain. It's protecting you from feeling the immensity of emotional pain, which you have, at some point, deemed more hurtful than physical pain. The body will take the brunt of the emotional trauma in the form of pain that won't go away or pain that seems to require surgery because for many, it's easier to deal with physical pain than emotional distress.

If this idea resonates with you, read on. If you're tired of pain and shame, turn the page.

WHEN THOUGHTS
CREATE PAIN

A FEW TIMES A YEAR, my family and I drove to the Poconos, the closest ski area to Philadelphia. Wedged between my dad's legs, we skied down the mountain. I vaguely remember it being fun—at five years of age, who connects with fear?

I was in first grade when we began going to Sun Valley, Idaho so that my brother Graham and I could get proper instruction. The second year we were there, the instructor stopped right in front of me mid-lesson while traversing a hill. Turning, she discovered me about to crash into her. "Oh wow, I didn't think you were right there. Normally, my students are way behind and I need to wait for them. You're rather advanced."

The statement surprised me. I was simply doing what I knew how to do. I was very coordinated and picked things up quickly, especially sports—something I took for granted. She noted that, without a doubt, I'd be skiing at Baldy Mountain the following year. That's where Mom and Dad skied. Graham, another natural athlete, had even made the

1

transition and skied there a few times that week. But I was in no hurry to move away from Elkhorn, the beginner's mountain, because my friends, the ones I'd made in ski school, and I would take jumps and ski the bowls, which was awfully fun.

Baldy was no joke. It's where the adults skied and you had to be really good to ski its slopes, or so I perceived. I didn't like the sound of Baldy. I liked being a big fish in a small pond, impressing the hell out of my friends and instructors. Baldy represented a bar I wasn't sure I could reach. There, I'd have to challenge myself and excel. Soon, I'd have to take on the double black diamonds full of moguls or super steep slopes, the kind I'd heard about or seen on TV or glimpsed at the Poconos while on the lift to other slopes, and that scared the bejesus out of me.

Two days before we departed Sun Valley, Graham entered a ski race. I'm pretty sure he came in first because of all the excitement and praise he got as a result. I stood by as he received a medal and my parents made a big to-do about it. They carried on with their effusive praise the following day, and all the way back to the airport. Sitting in the car, I felt as though all my parents could do was show excitement for Graham's win. Next to him, I felt like the world's biggest invisible loser. My instructor's praise evaporated into thin air. There was no point in mentioning it ever again.

These days, I think the participation trophies handed out to kids are pathetic. How will a child ever learn how to be a good loser? Yet looking back, and remembering how badly I wanted my parents' acknowledgement that I was worthy of praise (not just Graham), I can't help but think a participation trophy would have done some good. Without it, Graham would always be the star athlete, the one who got all the attention.

Later that spring, just before school let out for the year, I found myself in gym class. A huge wrestling mat had been placed on the floor for some activity or another, which required us eight-year-old kids to work as a team to roll it up. Everyone was having fun with the task until my good friend, Bekah, shrieked in pain. One of her feet had gotten caught inside the mat as everyone else was rolling it up.

Bekah went to the nurse's office and when she returned, she had crutches. All the kids went over to her to ask how she was feeling, genuinely concerned for her well-being.

Like that, a light bulb went off for me. *That's what I'm going to do. Next year, when I get back to school, I'm going to pretend to have pain so that Mom and Dad will finally give me some attention.* I thought about the possible afflictions I could fake and decided that it had to be something visible, just like Bekah's injury, to generate the same kind of loving concern.

The idea took on a life of its own. The added benefits of an injury occurred to me one by one. Being sick in my family meant staying home from school and being allowed to watch TV in bed. Graham and I weren't allowed a lot of TV. Normally, we'd watch various cartoons or children's programs when we'd come home from school, if Mom wasn't home; but when sick, it was a basic free for all. When either of us was sick with the cold or the flu, Mom would bring us tea and snacks. She'd give me extra care, which I ate up. And Graham couldn't rough house or tease me, which was probably my favorite form of dispensation.

The first day of third grade arrived. I hadn't forgotten my plan. I decided that limping home from the bus stop would make someone take notice. A neighbor kid shared my stop and I thought that maybe his housekeeper or nanny or whomever the woman was who sometimes met him might take notice and tell my mom. I repeated my limping act for a number of days to no avail. Eventually, when I decided to speed things up, I complained to Mom that my feet hurt. That wasn't enough to get her to take notice, so I stepped it up and decided to get other teachers to believe in my imaginary discomfort.

In my after-school ballet class, I told my teacher, whom I adored, that my feet hurt; at gymnastics, another activity that filled my schedule, I pretended my hands hurt and I couldn't do a handstand or roundoff. I left tennis and horseback riding alone, choosing to act like normal, but ballroom dancing was my least favorite of all. There, I basically acted like I'd suffered a stroke and hadn't learned to walk and talk again.

That prompted Mom to take me to a number of doctors who all did their exams and told her, "Your daughter is in perfect health."

About two months into my charade, while in my parents' bedroom, my dad asked me sternly, "Serena, are you really in pain?"

It was the first time he asked me directly about what I might have been feeling. Mom had been concerned and was the one taking me to doctors and getting feedback from my after-school activity instructors. I looked Dad right in the eyes and lied. "Yes."

He threw up his hands as if to say, "No further questions." I should probably mention here that I was dealing with a high-powered attorney, not just my dad, which would explain his demeanor.

In mid-November, I was excited to take a field trip to a chocolate factory not far from school. We were promised a chocolate at the end of the tour. It seemed like we were almost there, but I couldn't make it. My feet felt really sore. I wondered if I had twisted an ankle, or stubbed a toe, then I thought maybe God was getting even with me for lying.

I began to cry. I told my teacher I wanted to sit down. That's when shit got real.

By mid-December, I'd been admitted to Children's Hospital. Instead of basking in the attention of my family and the nursing staff, I hated being in the hospital, eating bland hospital food, and being surrounded by sick kids. I wasn't sick. I, the natural athlete, certainly didn't need to be in a wheelchair to get labs done. I wanted to stand up as if to say, "See? I can walk!" Instead, I stayed quiet.

I was now along for the ride, a ride I suspected I had created. As much as I didn't enjoy doctors poking and prodding me and being asked to bend my legs and walk down the hall as they watched, I had gotten what I wanted. I decided to ride it out, to see how much I could milk it even though I truly was in pain.

When doctors asked me to bend my knees and squat down to check my range of motion, I surprised myself when it was difficult to do just that. My range of motion had, oddly enough, decreased. I figured it wouldn't be permanent though. I'd have pain for a bit, maybe until the end of the school year, get my parents to finally see me and pay me equal attention to Graham, and then I'd go back to being the pain-free athlete I knew myself to be. I had no real understanding of my diagnosis; I had developed Juvenile Rheumatoid Arthritis (JRA).

Right after being released from the hospital, as a celebration, my parents took me to see the Harlem Globetrotters. It was a lot of fun. And I scored in the sympathy department. Upon returning home, I found friends from school and friends of my parents had all sent cards and gifts. I loved all the concern. The pain was real, but the benefits of having it far outweighed the consequences I had to suffer through.

I dabbled with forgoing any pain relief so I could keep the attention flowing. Before trying any major medication, I was given eight chewable baby aspirin to take four times a day to reduce the pain and inflammation. I wasn't about to give up my hard-won attention so sometimes, when my mom wasn't looking, I'd hide some in a tissue box near my bed. That little trick backfired when Mom found it and confronted me.

"Serena, I found your aspirin in your tissue box. You have to take them. They will help you get better. Why are you hiding them?"

"I don't like taking them. I'm tired of it. They're not making me feel better. What's the use?" I replied.

"If you don't take them you'll feel worse," she told me. "Let's try the aspirin before stronger medication, OK?"

A few months after that, my parents went on vacation and left Graham and me at our grandmother's. I wasn't in crisis anymore. Doctors had given me a diagnosis and were trying to manage the pain and get me better. I had gone back to school and had become one of the worst athletes, no longer picked first during gym class, no more after-school sports. People went back to their normal lives.

I had learned from my first failed attempt at hiding the aspirin that I needed to be craftier. I was now on a stronger medication, despite the suggestion that I could avoid this if I took the aspirin. I was concerned that the pills would make me well again, and I'd go back to playing second fiddle in my family, and not measure up. I'd take my pills from my grandma when she handed them to me at lunchtime and hide them in the paper napkin. Later, I'd walk outside and throw the pills over her backyard wall. I figured that by the time the snow melted, the pills would have disintegrated too.

In the year or so after the diagnosis, there were times I tried to make the JRA go away, using mind over matter techniques, the way I felt I brought it on, but it didn't budge. Nothing changed. Eventually, we all got used to the idea, and my parents got busy. I had become 'Serena with Juvenile Rheumatoid Arthritis,' and it had become the new normal.

JAW OPERATION

MY JAW RECEDED INWARDS, A common issue in children with JRA, and my front and bottom teeth had a space between them when they closed, something braces couldn't fix (even after a few years of trying). So, they deemed reconstructive jaw surgery the final resort.

In tenth grade, my peers were starting to date and my body was changing. I felt self-conscious about my looks in general. From sixth grade on, my face looked puffier, rounder when I compared it to those of my friends. I didn't like the way I looked but I didn't think I was exactly hideous. In other words, I was like most girls my age. (Years later, I was horrified to see photos from that era, not just because I looked far worse than I realized, but because they reminded me of how conflicted I was about my appearance.) Just like the arthritis, I didn't focus all of my attention on how different I was from the other kids; I didn't preoccupy my time looking at my face in the mirror and wondering why I didn't look like my friends. Thankfully, nobody ever bullied me about it either.

Despite my insecurity, I argued about having the operation, which I simply did not want. It was my mom's decision to find a specialist and to do something about my bite. I wanted more time to consider my options. My mom wanted the operation done sooner rather than later.

During dinner one night, my mom and I got into an argument about whether I needed the operation and I told her I didn't want it. Not at that time. She told me I did. I stormed away from the patio table, where we were having dinner.

Upstairs, I eavesdropped on the subsequent conversation. I could see and hear them from the open window in my parents' bedroom but they couldn't see me. I overheard my mom ask my brother, "How will she ever get a boyfriend if she doesn't get the operation?" Graham looked off into the distance and didn't answer. My dad didn't comment either. He stared into space, no doubt thinking his own thoughts, as he often did when the conversation didn't involve him.

I was devastated. I had no idea my mom was ashamed of how I looked, at least that's how I interpreted her comment. Until that moment, I never realized she was critical of my appearance. She would tell me she didn't like what I was wearing or would tell me that certain outfits were unflattering, but she never told me I was so ugly that men would never want to date me. It dawned on me that my deformed face was reflecting badly on her and if I didn't change my face—the first thing people saw—she wouldn't accept me, and neither would men.

Years later, I told my mom how hurtful it was to hear her say those words. "I would never say anything like that," she said.

I don't think I made up what she said. Why would I?

Why would I imagine my mom saying something that for years pierced my heart? All the same, that's what I remember and that's how I interpreted it.

The operation was five hours long. Immediately afterwards, I was placed in the Intensive Care Unit (ICU) and given a button to call the nurse for morphine to ease the pain. A day later, I was transferred to a room. I didn't see myself in the mirror until three days post-operation. I cried. I was grotesque. I looked like the Elephant Man. My face was five times its normal size and I had bruises along my jaw that had turned to yellow and blue. The nurse helping me to the bathroom (now that the catheter was out) gave me a little hug.

At home, my mom helped feed me the first two weeks. I was unable to talk or eat solid food. I could only get nutrients from liquid as I couldn't open my jaw much at all. She would feed me through a straw and most of the liquid would end up on my face or anywhere but inside my mouth. She seemed to enjoy being my caretaker. She would sit near my bed and read me Charles Dickens's *A Tale of Two Cities*. I preferred watching TV all day. It was an escape from my anger and mortification. No one had prepared me for how ugly I would look or how dependent I would become on my mom.

Two weeks later, when we returned to the doctor who'd performed the surgery, my mom asked him, "Did you fix her nose? It looks better, too."

He told her no, "Her nose may look different due to the structure of her jaw."

My face was swollen for almost eleven months. Little by little my face and entire head went from being a few times bigger than its normal size to decreasing to a normal size head. There's a photo of me beaming at the Greenbrier where my parents gave me the gift of attending a culinary class for a long weekend. I dreamed of being a chef. Despite my huge head, I looked happy.

I had to get back to normalcy. Just like before the operation, I didn't notice my arthritic hands every minute of the day, but I was reminded of them whenever I couldn't open something. Same with the swollen face. I had to get on with life and not be upset with my mom and the world.

I went to a small, private Quaker school, where all the kids were nice and no one made fun of me. I wasn't reminded of what I saw in the mirror. I had a few close friends, but I never discussed the jaw operation and never told anyone about the comments my mom had made.

IT WAS KISMET:
MEETING LILI

To get to the heart of the matter, let's jump ahead a bit . . .

When I returned for my junior year of college, I decided to live off campus. One of the first things I did was join a gym—24 Hour Fitness. After explaining to the woman who signed me up about my arthritis, she told me she knew of a fantastic massage therapist and proceeded to write Lili's name and number on the back of her card. I kept that card on my desk from August through March and would often pick it up, look at the name and number on the back, and never do anything about it.

In March, my back was killing me. I didn't know what had brought it on and figured too many hours of studying was likely the culprit. I looked at the card and called the number. The voicemail I left went something like this:

"Hi Lili, my name is Serena and I've been having horrible back pain. I've had arthritis for many years so I'm not sure how you can help, but thought I'd see if you have any time when I can come in for a session. Here's my number . . ."

I'm not sure how you can help. The back pain was so bad I had become pessimistic. I didn't want her to think I had all my eggs in her basket. I wanted her to know that I didn't expect her to find the cure. I was used to finding a therapist of some sort who would help me feel better, but then there would be a plateau and the symptoms would return, which would cause me to search for other answers and other practitioners.

After my first visit with Lili, I felt better. She told me if I had not come in, if I had left my body to deal with the pain on its own, I could have injured myself reaching for the phone—a landline, of course, since this was pre-mobile phone—given the tightness of my muscles.

I continued to see her and then I stopped. I figured the relief I got would be as good as I could get and there was no reason to keep seeing her.

Lili had asked who else I'd seen for the arthritis and back pain. The truth was, I didn't have any regular practitioners in my contact list at the time. I knew how to stretch on my own and I saw a lady the year before who had me walk around with a TENS machine that sent electric currents up my back, but it didn't make me feel better. I visited an acupuncturist for a series of sessions and while he got my odd foot pain feeling better, I didn't feel any different in my joints. At a certain point, I didn't think that anyone else could make the arthritis go away—I've always clung to the belief that since I created it, that job was up to me. Of course, I still needed other practitioners to keep me feeling tension-free.

After a while, Lili called to follow up. She gave it to me straight.

"You go from one practitioner to another and leave before anyone can fully try and help you. My guess is that you'll take a break from me and then go find someone else and keep up this routine until you get tired and then find some other healer. My recommendation is to stick with me and see how good you can feel."

I needed that. I needed someone to confront my pattern. She was direct and I appreciated that. Because she was the first one to call me on my behavior, I listened. But she was also warm and nurturing. Lili was the first type of holistic healer to really believe in me. She understood how the mind can create illness and alleviate pain as well and she completely accepted my rationale for how the arthritis had developed.

She would press on a certain knot in my back, ask me to rate it from one to five, then instruct me to focus on it while breathing. When she guided me through dissolving pain this way, I found the tension vanished within seconds. I thought the technique was pretty cool. In response, she told me she'd never worked with someone like me, someone who had such laser-like focus to eradicate pain from the body quickly. That felt good. Really good. She was basically reinforcing the belief I held about my ability to create pain in my body. I had developed a fascination for the mind's ability to create pain, having personally experienced it; now someone saw me do that action in reverse, to get out of pain.

But she also told me my gift was a double-edged sword. If I decided that she wasn't going to help me that day, no matter what she did or what tools she tried to use with me, the knot and tension wouldn't budge. It was all on me, according to Lili, and what I chose to do with my mind.

About a year after seeing her consistently, she introduced me to Dr. Allen Knecht, a chiropractor. She explained his technique involved muscle testing, where he would ask my body about certain emotions to alleviate pain within a few minutes. She was fascinated by the muscle testing alone and tried to show me, but hadn't been trained in it at the time. She suggested I see Dr. Knecht for the full experience. I was skeptical but I had developed a deeper relationship with Lili and trusted that she wouldn't lead me astray. She also told me that she had learned about Dr. Knecht from one of her clients. This client had suffered severe back issues and then all of a sudden, the client stopped coming in. When she returned six months later, her back had dramatically improved. When Lili asked her what she had done, she informed her about Dr. Knecht and his techniques. I was intrigued.

I went to see him and was amazed. By pressing on my arm and asking me to say or think about various things he could make my arm weak.

"Repeat after me," he'd say.

"My name is Serena."

My arm was strong when I said that sentence.

"My name is Jonathan."

My arm went weak when I repeated that sentence.

"I'm OK healing this pain."

My arm went weak.

When I was OK with a certain statement, my body was strong, as shown by pressing on my arm; but when I wasn't OK with a statement, my body was weak. My arm was weak when I said my name was Jonathan, because that's not my name and my body was not congruent with what my mind knew. But weakness in response to, "I'm OK healing this pain," meant there were emotions getting in the way of why I felt I couldn't heal the pain. Not a good thing to discover about yourself. With that insight in mind, Dr. Knecht went after the emotions beneath my pain. He was able to find them by identifying the emotions to which I was reacting and why.

Once he helped me figure that out the arm would be strong again, which would allow my body and mind to feel better.

I continued to see Dr. Knecht until I left Portland for England a year after graduating from college.

Lili remained a constant in my life for about seven years. As a life coach, which was one of the healing roles she played over the years, she really helped me understand how reactive I was, and the effect my emotions had on my body. She used a system to help me understand how to get out of my own way based on a book by psychologist Vern Black, PhD. In *Love Me? Love Yourself* (cheesy title, I know), Black explains the principles of the Integrity Tone Scale, which is a roadmap for understanding how you're feeling and reacting in your mind. In order to have a more positive outcome, the tone scale shows the steps for transforming your thoughts.

Lili also suggested I sign up for a two-day event called the Liberty Experience (which is where she first discovered Black's book). She mentioned that their more advanced courses worked off the tone scale, but even their basic course would give me some ideas for healing the arthritis. She didn't want to give away too much because she wanted me to experience it rather than understand it intellectually.

The Liberty Experience was similar to the Landmark Forum, a personal development system that challenges various ways of thinking. The Liberty Experience suggests that the meaning and interpretation we place on events create our experiences and consequent interpretations. We then live from those experiences even if our interpretations are not true or accurate. It's the reason why we end up dissatisfied in our relationships; we don't tell the truth. We'd rather be right about what we make up, than take responsibility for our faulty thoughts. We also don't want to admit we're wrong, because that never feels good.

I went through the program but didn't have a breakthrough like so many of the other participants. Still, I was curious about the system. I started to see how closed down I was, how shy and timid and how little confidence I felt in the world. One participant even pointed out that I would always look at her lips rather than her eyes when talking, even though I wasn't deaf and lip reading. I was too shy to maintain eye contact.

A few months later, I decided to take the Liberty Experience again, this time in San Francisco, as opposed to Portland. This time I had a breakthrough. During one of the exercises, we were being taught how to do Holotropic Breathwork. Lying on a mat, eyes closed, in a low-lit room with ambient music, doing accelerated breathing, I had some sort of epiphany. I told one of the facilitators that back when I was eight and pretending to have pain, it felt as though I had taken on a role, that of someone in pain. By doing so, I had entered a parallel universe or some other dimension where I assumed that role by believing with full conviction that I was in pain and then, in a very short time, got what I wanted. The next day the facilitator brought me a book, *The Law and The Promise* by Neville Goddard, who wrote and spoke on the topic of how imagination creates reality. I devoured that book and ended up ordering every other book he wrote. His books were repetitive and had far too many biblical quotes for me, but he is, nonetheless, an author who changed my life.

At the time the book was given to me, I thought it was a little far-fetched. Neville, as he was known, explained that everything you have in your life is a result of having imagined it first, whether consciously or unconsciously. He gave clear directions on how to use the power of the mind to alter reality so you can manifest your desires. He described how to imagine your goal with all your senses and feel what it would be like to have already achieved your desires. The key was to feel from what he called "the wish fulfilled," from the end result rather than in the wishing of it (where you still didn't have what you wanted).

I realized that was precisely what I had done to create the arthritis. I imagined that I was already in pain to convince others of my act until I started to truly feel it myself.

Years later, *The Law of Attraction* and *The Secret* came out, but neither came close to getting at the core of the phenomena I had used as a child and have been trying to turn on again ever since. No psychologist or psychotherapist was as effective at helping me transform and push past my comfort zone since Lili, and I've sat with plenty. As a requirement for grad school, I had to see a therapist for fifty-five hours. To satisfy that requirement, I saw about five different professionals over six years. I stuck with Lili for years; it didn't matter where—I saw her even when I lived in London, New York City, and San Francisco.

I don't know where I'd be or how different my life would be if I hadn't met her. She was the catalyst for so much of my healing.

CLIENT CASE: SHANNON

SHANNON WAS TWENTY-SEVEN YEARS OLD when she came to see me for anxiety verging on constant panic attacks. Her girlfriend accompanied her to the session and filled in any holes that needed more detail. They disclosed that they both had enjoyed partying in their younger years, going to raves and taking Ecstasy every weekend, but they hadn't done any drugs for over five years.

Since she was a child, Shannon felt some level of anxiety and depression. Over the years, however, that anxiety had become much worse, prompting her to seek medication. Initially, she found relief and felt better. But within a year, the meds stopped working—the dose would need to be increased or she would need to change medications. She didn't like knowing that the medication would eventually lose its effectiveness, but she was desperate, so she'd start the cycle again. Soon enough, the latest round of meds stopped working, and four months later, no switch or increase would do the trick.

That's when she showed up in my office.

I asked her to describe more of her history, how often she went to raves, how many times she took Ecstasy in a month or on a weekend. From there, I asked her whether she felt the anxiety had been present before she began attending raves. At what point in her life had she started to really notice it?

According to her, she'd always been rather shy and introverted during high school. In college, she'd found a niche group of friends where she felt fully accepted. Shannon suggested that she felt more depression in high school and more anxiety after college.

How did the anxiety and depression affect her life? What did it prevent her from doing or having? These were just a few of my initial questions. I wanted to fully understand how her issues created a deficit in her life, how it impacted her day-to-day living and overall well-being. Did it cause difficulty in her career, with her friendships, or with her girlfriend?

She reported that she had developed agoraphobia, an anxiety disorder characterized by fear of places that seem unsafe, especially ones that lack an easy way out. She hadn't gone grocery shopping for six months. "You can't see the exits when you're in a supermarket," she said.

Shannon also explained that driving was too terrifying for her. She felt like the other cars would get too close to her and she would start to panic and imagine the worst. Agoraphobia causes people to fear situations where they feel helpless, trapped, embarrassed, and unable to get out. Sometimes, people end up rarely leaving their homes because most public places elicit too much anxiety.

Her girlfriend had picked up much of the slack.

Because Shannon felt depressed and anxious much of the time, she wasn't working. It was too stressful to be around other people and she feared her boss would criticize her work to such a degree that she would be unable to feel like she held any value to her company. *Was she being criticized that much?* I wondered. I inquired and it turned out that it was more the anticipation of being told she was a bad employee that felt paralyzing.

Lethargy, frustration, sadness, shame, guilt—these were all feelings Shannon felt daily. She added despair to the mix, when she met a medication impasse.

I suspected that her serotonin levels were toast, that she'd likely fried them during her rave days. Whatever anti-anxiety medications and antidepressants she'd tried had no doubt boosted her levels, but the temporary fix had been synthetic. No one had assessed the root cause of her ailments. Why had she become so deflated and unable to function? What prior experience or relationship might have contributed to her inability to move forward with courage despite setbacks or critical remarks? These were the questions going through my mind.

To begin with, I had her repeat a few 'OK' statements, such as "I'm OK," "I'm OK without anxiety," "It's OK to be happy." I found a number of emotions in response to these statements including fear of the future, avoidance, powerlessness, hopelessness, worthlessness, and loss of purpose. I asked her how each emotion made sense in light of what she was experiencing. She claimed they all resonated because they depicted how she felt about being in the world. She blamed herself for taking too many drugs when she was younger, opting for the high of the moment and not thinking of the long-term effects. Consequently, she had become unable to function like everyone else and the relief she received from the meds was always transitory, which made her feel like life in general only held glimpses of joy and excitement.

When we traced these emotions back to an earlier time, her muscle went weak at age eleven. Her parents had recently divorced and on the days or weekends she had to live with her dad, she never knew if he'd be OK or a monster. She used to be happy at school, but the walk home and the anticipation of what kind of mood he'd be in really caused her stress. Some days she'd come home and sit quietly in her room, doing her homework or reading or watching TV, but she never knew what her dad would be like when he called her into the living room. On the days he'd been drinking to excess, he'd hit her. When she tried to run, he would grab her by her arms or legs, shout in her face, and throw her across the room like a rag doll. He'd pick her up from wherever she landed and do it again and again until he spent his rage, not hearing the terror and pleading in her voice.

As she recalled the horror of those memories, I identified more emotions. Feeling alone, disconnected from the mind and body, overwhelmed, withdrawn, emotionally disengaged, numb, emotional loss, false sense of security, worry, need for love and attention. As I told her these emotions, she described other memories around the same time when she had been the victim of similar abuse.

Eventually these emotions changed to ones of anger, resentment, gall, and being furious with her dad for treating her that way, and for no one coming to her defense.

Shannon told me that she hadn't thought of those memories in years. Her girlfriend said she knew of Shannon's family background but had no idea of the extent of what she'd gone through.

I explained that all the feelings of being victimized, abused, and severely neglected physically and emotionally as a child caused her to shut off from her mind and body. In order to survive and truly get through the shock and trauma, she had to disengage from her emotions and any need she had for love or respect. Her needs weren't worthy. She wasn't of value to her dad beyond serving as a target for his rage. As a result, she'd repressed all those feelings—of being worthless, fearing a future in which he could continue abusing her, never knowing if he would use her as his punching bag, or simply ignore her instead. She felt she had no purpose and hadn't since she was as an eleven-year-old child.

People take drugs for all types of reasons and Shannon said she took Ecstasy as a way to escape the memories and feelings of low self-esteem, shame, sadness, and despair. She wanted a prescription medication to numb those feelings as well, but her body had built up a tolerance, perhaps as a way to force her to look at what was hiding underneath and to heal those old wounds.

The following week I had her on my schedule so I could give her my report of findings. I looked in the waiting room, but didn't see Shannon or her girlfriend. At ten minutes past the scheduled time, I asked the receptionist to call and find out why she was late or whether she was going to make the appointment. She told me that Shannon was in the waiting room. I looked again.

"That's not her."

"Yes it is. She checked in five minutes early."

I walked into the waiting room and approached the couple. After a few seconds, I recognized the girlfriend, but really had to stare at Shannon to make sense of what I saw. As we walked to my office, I was baffled. Why did Shannon look so different, almost unrecognizable?

It began to make sense when I asked Shannon to tell me how she felt after the session the week before. She and her girlfriend excitedly told me that upon returning home that day, she slept for twelve hours; the next day she did ten loads of laundry, drove to the grocery store and bought groceries—both of which she hadn't done in months—then proceeded to clean the house for the next few days. They decided they both enjoyed cleaning and organizing so much that they would open a cleaning business and call it OCD Cleaning.

GRAHAM, GRAHAM, GRAHAM

YOU REMEMBER ME DESCRIBING THIS scene. On the morning of September 11, 2001, I was on my way to my office. I got stuck in the subway at Wall Street Station. When we were allowed to exit the station, the first tower had fallen. Smoke and ash were everywhere and I couldn't see more than five feet in front of me. I think that's when I went into shock; although the scariest part of that whole day was being in the train. It had stopped. The motor was off and I thought there was a fire in the station. Smoke filled the platform and no one was around. My pulse was racing.

Once we made it to street level, I followed the other passengers down Wall Street since I couldn't see where I was going and FBI agents were herding us that way. About twenty minutes later, while walking north with throngs of other people, I watched the second tower collapse.

Ash covered my hair and clothes as I walked five miles home.

My mom had left me four voicemails, but the cell phones

25

were dead. Midway through my journey home, I saw a line of people at payphones. I decided to call my apartment hoping my friend who was staying with me would pick up. She did and I told her to call my mom.

But here's what I didn't mention before. After arriving back at my apartment, my friend told me I should call my parents. I worked myself up to the task by forcing myself to be calm. Meaning, I choked back any emotions so they wouldn't erupt and cause me to cry. I felt like my legs were still shaking from earlier that day and I didn't want to break down into tears. It simply didn't feel emotionally safe to do so.

By the time I called my parents, they had already learned that I was safe thanks to my friend. They asked about my experience. My dad said, "You were so close. What did you see?"

That was it. Of course, they were inquisitive, but I just wanted them to say, "We're so relieved you're OK. We were so worried."

What I got from my mom left me feeling worse.

"At least you didn't have to go through what Graham did. He saw people jumping. He watched the towers come down. It was awful for him."

Mind you, my brother had watched the whole event unfold from Jersey City.

"Mom! I was there. I was two blocks away. I saw FBI officers wearing gas masks, yelling at us to run for our lives. I could see and hear the tower collapsing. I walked by lines of people standing at hospitals to donate blood. I stood in one. Why was it harder for Graham?"

Even while recounting such a horrific event as 9/11, I still felt like I was competing for my mom's attention, that no matter my experience, Graham got more concern. It didn't matter what I went through. I didn't matter. Graham was always going to have the attention and concern.

Earlier that year (2001), my brother's girlfriend of two and a half years broke up with him. He didn't handle it well. In fact, he became so depressed that a concerned friend reached out to my parents. My parents dropped everything and drove to New York City, where he was living. I was in London for journalism school and they implored me to call him and offer my support, despite the fact that Graham and I never talked. I left him a heartfelt message but my mom, frantic, tripped over his answering machine upon entering his apartment and accidentally erased it. She had a key and let herself in when he was at work and waited for him to come home while my dad walked around the city.

When Graham arrived, according to her, they had a heart to heart and she suggested that Dad's competitive nature was at the root of Graham's depression. At least she had an answer that let Graham (and her) off the hook.

Now, it may seem a small thing to anger me like it did, but there's more to my response than meets the eye . . .

You see, I became depressed in the twelfth grade. Looking back, it's easy to see why. I had just undergone a drastic change to my appearance and hadn't talked to anyone about what I went through. By the time the swelling was finally gone, it didn't seem to be enough for my mom. Instead, she told me I still had a lisp at times, that the jaw operation hadn't fixed it; then she made me go to speech therapy to correct it. That, in and of itself, was mortifying. Try staring at your mouth in a mirror, watching the way you make 'ch' and 'sh' sounds and see if you don't wish you could crawl into a hole and die. The way I spoke wasn't acceptable. "What will colleges or jobs think?" she asked me. She was always concerned with how I looked, never how I was doing emotionally.

But I didn't understand any of it at the time. All I knew was that I was unhappy with my life. I'd come home after the tennis team, do my stretching in the basement, and cry. For the first time, I started imagining ending my life. I finally worked up the courage to tell my mom I was having suicidal ideations. We were in the kitchen, me at the counter, she doing dishes. She laughed and said, "That's just teen angst. You'll get over it."

Maybe she didn't believe I was truly suicidal, but it never even occurred to her to ask me why I felt the way I did. It was as though she had never felt depressed before, and if it wasn't in her repertoire, it was impossible for her to understand how someone else could feel that way. It was easier to brush off. She couldn't hear me and understand me. She lacked empathy when I needed it most. That moment taught me, cemented in place, that I couldn't go to my mom to help process my emotional reactions, so I stuffed those feelings even more.

Clearly, it was a different story with my brother. In such circumstances, it's hard not to suspect favoritism. Granted, his friend saw how poorly he coped and was concerned enough that she told my parents. I, alone, told my mom how depressed I felt; I didn't get other people involved. I'll give you that.

Graham and I have never seen eye to eye—in part due to the perceived favoritism; in part due to his personality disorders, of which I feel he has two. When you live with someone with certain disorders, you learn to keep your feelings to yourself.

Before the events transpired in New York City, Mom and I drove cross-country to Reed College. It was a fun adventure. Although she got on my nerves from time to time, we had a good trip. She helped me set up my dorm room, and I walked her to the car. Before she got in the car, I told her I loved her. It was the first time I ever uttered those words to her. She looked at me with eyes brimming with tears, but she didn't say it back; she got in the car and drove off. I've told my mom "I love you" three times in my life and have never heard it back. I'm OK with that. When you grow up never hearing those words, you start to understand they're just words.

The first few days at college I was already homesick. I called home thinking that Mom was already there, and Graham picked up the phone. I asked to talk to Mom. When he said she wasn't there, I was on the verge of tears.

"It sounds like you're about to cry," he laughed. "What's wrong, are you homesick?" He laughed again and scoffed in his condescending manner.

I wasn't about to give him what he wanted, which was to make me cry and feel worse. I pushed the feelings away so I wouldn't feel them.

Over time, this became a reflex; my MO was to be detached, because I'd learned that my feelings didn't matter and it felt awful to have them, especially when they weren't acknowledged. In other words, I taught myself how to not feel.

But the feelings didn't evaporate as I wanted them to. They got lodged in my body and I felt pain in my joints. That's what the body does as a means of self-protection. For a lot of people with chronic pain, their emotions are too upsetting to feel. It's easier to deal with physical pain.

I didn't make this connection until a few years later, but many people still view pain and emotional reactions as separate. It's similar to food and bloating; it seems obvious to me that a certain food has a negative effect when the result of eating it is a distended belly, but many people still don't make that connection.

A few years post 9/11, after my brother's breakup, he got sick. I won't go into the details, but it was pretty serious. I believe his illness developed due to his own repressed anger about his breakup with his girlfriend a few years earlier, which, as his actions belied, he didn't take very well. He wanted to marry her and have a family.

After the breakup, he sought the help of a social worker and went through therapy. While he was getting psychological help, his whole demeanor changed. He became softer, curious about how his upbringing and relationships shaped him. But it was ephemeral. To me, it seems he got scared of what he was uncovering so he stopped getting help and went back to being a cold-hearted impenetrable piece of rock. Any semblance of closeness was eclipsed by his inability to be with his uncomfortable emotions and do something about them, or so it appeared to me.

Even though I'll likely never be friends with Graham, I can't help but notice—he's not done all that well with his emotions either.

CLIENT CASE: EMMA

Soon after tying the knot at age thirty, Emma had developed pain that caused her to be bedridden. Normally very active, being unable to walk down a flight of stairs without creating major discomfort caused her to feel depressed and hopeless.

Being a personal trainer (like many of my clients), she was already well-versed in diet, nutrition, and strength programs. Then she came across John Sarno's work and identified with his diagnosis of Tension Myositis Syndrome (TMS) and treatment plan. John Sarno, a medical doctor, wrote three books on the topic of physical pain, especially back pain, being the result of unexpressed emotions. Although he's not the first doctor to suggest this, he coined the TMS diagnosis, and, through his books and articles, reached and helped many people with his findings.

By following Dr. Sarno's recommendations, Emma was able to cure herself of debilitating pain.

Seven years later, however, the pain returned, this time

to her hips. She recognized, thanks to Sarno's writings, that because its origin is linked to emotional factors, the pain will often shift from one area of the body to another in what is known as Symptom Imperative. If someone is able to make the pain go away in the knee, for example, but the emotional factor causing the pain hasn't been fully addressed, it will show up in another part of the body until the issue is finally resolved.

Emma's pain kept shifting from one area to the next until, exasperated, she contacted me.

Within the first few sessions, I identified emotions such as shame, awkwardness, confusion, self-consciousness, powerless, and feeling locked inside. As we began working together, I asked her to describe how she resonated with those feelings. Initially, she explained that the pain she was presently experiencing reminded her of the symptoms she had when she was newly married. She felt helpless to get better after countless doctors' visits and many alternative treatments had failed. She described the frustration of being convinced that the achiness in her body was due to repressed emotions but couldn't figure out what they were. As I found other emotions, I soon discovered they were connected to her dad. I asked Emma to explain how being unable to share, withdrawal from communication, feeling unsafe, lost, vulnerable, and resentful were linked to her dad. She paused and then burst into tears.

"My dad is an alcoholic. I'm so ashamed of this. No one outside of my family knows. Even my closest friends have no clue. And when I try to talk to my dad and get him to do something about it, he gets defensive and then my siblings get mad at me because I've ruined the night. So, we all just let him drink."

Her dad's drinking was tormenting Emma, whereas her siblings seemed more preoccupied with their own lives. I asked Emma to really get in touch with how her dad's alcoholism was disrupting her own life.

I was curious about the changes she'd made in response to her dad's drinking. Emma knew precisely what I was after. She planned her visits when she knew that her dad would be sober. She imagined that if she had kids, she'd make sure they would only visit early enough in the day to ensure that her dad hadn't yet cracked open a case of beer.

Although she tried having a conversation with her mom to enlist her help, those endeavors also left her feeling frustrated. Everyone was letting Emma's dad drink to excess and spoil the day or evening spent together; no one was telling her dad that it wasn't OK. As a result, Emma held all the resentment, concern, and sadness in her body.

Finally, I told her, "Emma, why is everyone in your family walking on eggshells around your dad? No one enjoys watching him get wasted. Your siblings limit the time their kids spend with him; you know you can only have heartfelt conversations with him at certain times of the day. Yet no one is telling him how you really feel about his drinking."

Emma explained that previous attempts had only put the burden on her. She'd been blamed for even bringing it up. The rest of the family, though not happy with the situation, had learned to deal with it and so Emma got the message that it was not OK to tell her dad how she really felt. She repressed her thoughts and feelings, even her reactions, but her body suffered. Since Emma relied on her body for her work as a personal trainer I told her that I could help her identify all the emotions connected to her dad's drinking; but ultimately, confronting her dad and expressing how it affected her would likely be the action needed to fully heal her mind and body.

Sometimes it's not enough to identify the cause of the pain. Sometimes, talking to that person in a way that is received is the necessary step. Even if that person has passed on, writing a letter, reading it out loud, and processing the emotions that arise often help release the emotional pain from the body.

As we uncovered the emotions stuck in her body, a lot of feelings were similar to how she felt growing up and being left alone when she was a child. When she was five, her dad's job as a pilot changed from doing commuter flights and being home for dinner to flying cross country and being gone a few days a week. Around the same time, her mom's job as a nurse changed to taking on a few night shifts. Emma had become accustomed to having her parents tuck her into bed and read her bedtime stories. Even though her grandmother stayed to look after Emma and her older, far more composed siblings, Emma felt completely abandoned. Every time her parents left, she feared they would never return.

How did this connect to her dad's current drinking problem? Just like when Emma was young and her siblings seemed to have a handle on their parents' absence, they also seemed to accept their dad's drinking—it was Emma who felt too much. Emma felt deserted by her dad when he was drinking because he wasn't emotionally available. While her dad was numbing his feelings, Emma felt like she didn't matter and kept those feelings to herself.

Sometimes the original event went back to various boyfriends, with Emma not wanting to hurt their feelings by communicating how she felt about something that upset her. But overall the theme was the same: don't rock the boat, don't upset them. Keep your feelings to yourself because it will only make things worse to voice your emotions.

Eventually, Emma developed the strength to approach her dad in a very loving manner and express to him how his drinking was causing her to be in pain. Emma's intervention got her dad to take the action he needed to work on his drinking problem. It didn't happen overnight. Yet the very act of Emma taking the necessary steps to approach her dad and describe how his drinking was not only numbing his own emotions, but making Emma assume she had to squelch her own, created the space for healing to occur.

UNDER THE THUMB

I'VE SPENT A LIFETIME TRYING to understand my mom, how she thinks, what makes her tick. If I understand her, maybe I'll understand myself. I'll understand the power she's held over me.

Sometime during grad school, having learned a thing or two about psychology through my studies, I thought I had the tools to get my mom to understand why I wanted to do something of which she disapproved. I don't recall the details; I only remember her disapproval. I wanted to have a rational conversation with her, like two adults, but I feared she'd be angry with me, even make me feel ashamed if I didn't agree with her plan for me. Emotional blackmail, that's what I called her strategy for control. No tool in my box was strong enough to counteract that.

The influence she had on me for much of my life embarrasses me still. To think of all the friends I let my mom steer me away from, the men I assumed she wouldn't want me to date, the places I shouldn't live, because she disapproved for this reason or another.

Every decision I made was unknowingly (but highly) influenced by my mom and whether I thought she'd approve. Actually, she was quite vociferous with her opinions, so there's that.

Over time, I began to internalize her criticism. When I considered my date's income, or whether I was pretty enough or too introverted, I wondered if it was my mom's judgment or my own. Often, I'd assume someone was criticizing me when they weren't at all, simply because what they said sounded like something that would fall out of my mom's mouth. I'd react negatively, even overreact, because I'd become so sensitive to my every character flaw—that's how adept she was at pointing them out. Not just my character flaws, but those of my friends, those of random people on the street. Perhaps I should have grown immune to it all, which could have been another outcome. Instead, I learned to tear myself apart.

Frankly, I never told Mom about the men I dated. On rare occasions she found out because I couldn't hide it. There was the Australian I dated for a summer, who stayed at my house; the guy I dated after my post doc whom she had met years before while I was in grad school, and whom she liked, but I just couldn't force an attraction. Even if she didn't meet the guy, her criticism seeped into my mind. What would she think of this guy—his career, how he dresses, how much money he makes, what kind of future he sees for himself?

Mom was impressed with medical doctors, what with her father and brother being doctors. Lawyers came second, because my dad was a lawyer. She decreed physicans and attorneys worthy of marriage.

There was no fighting it, not really. I didn't have the power. I stood to lose too much if I defied her. I would lose her approval; and in its place I would feel shame, one of the worst emotions to feel. Shame, that's the emotion she inspired.

How did I allow her to gain that much power over me?

She wanted to see me get ahead, which doesn't sound all that abnormal, but I couldn't help but feel she wanted my success to make her look good. Instead of pushing me to make money, she encouraged me to go for experiences. To her way of thinking, the money would come later, when I had some job skills under my belt. If I just took any old job for money, I wouldn't advance. That's why I could intern at magazines in New York City during college; future journalism jobs would look upon this fondly.

I had lots of experiences, but no money of my own. That's how the power balance got tipped. When you get hooked on financial support like that, well, you'll do almost anything to keep it. You let those who support you weigh in.

Take my decision to live in different cities. Mom never liked me living in Portland, Oregon, which is where I got my bachelor's degree. She called it Cow-town because it wasn't cosmopolitan enough. She didn't mind me going to college there, but hated the fact that I wanted to live there afterwards. What would people think? How would she be viewed if she couldn't tell people her daughter was living in a major city? Would they assume she had a backward daughter who couldn't make it in a more advanced metropolis?

Perhaps her disapproval had to do with her master plan. She wanted me to pursue writing of some sort. She'd thought I had a knack for it in high school. I didn't see it but, hell, I didn't have much direction and I enjoyed reading and writing so I pursued an English Literature major at college. Perhaps she hoped I'd end up being a writer in New York City. If I had gone down that track, she'd be able to boast to her friends. And even if writing wasn't a boast-worthy career, like business or medicine, she could at least feel proud that I was living in New York City, where she had been an actress and a stockbroker. In her mind, New York City was the only place to live, even if I wasn't enamored with the place.

I presented my argument, quoting the New York University educated editor and journalist who hired me for an internship while I was in college:

"Mom, I think Elizabeth might know more on this subject given that she earned a master's in journalism from one of the top schools and has worked for a number of well-known national magazines. She said I'd get so much experience working at a small newspaper and covering every beat. I could do that for a year or two and have some clips to show magazines in New York City when I'm done."

I thought this argument made perfect sense. Obviously, I should stay in Portland and continue with the magazine where I worked, or even return to Portland after a journalism degree or even a master's in English Literature, which was my plan.

My mom had other ideas and she had every intention of cutting me off at the pass. "Why work in some small city when you can go to New York City and start gaining experience there?"

She claimed, teeth clenched, that working in New York City, at any national publication that would have me, was best; even if I never wrote any articles, at least I'd have a position on the masthead. That's where journalism is, after all: New York City. If I wanted to make it in journalism I might as well go to the center of it all, even if I didn't care to go.

And like that, I folded like a cheap suit—a resentful, angry, cheap suit. To make my surrender acceptable, I developed self-doubt. What did I know anyway? That's how self-doubt develops. It starts in one area and then it seeps into the rest.

It began long before this particular crossroad; we'd been arguing about my desire to stay in Portland for quite some time.

She had a meltdown after I finished college the year before. I was spent, completely burned out after graduation. I got through the coursework in four years and decided to take a year off from grad school. I had been accepted into two schools in England: Durham and Manchester University. Despite wanting a career in journalism, I thought a master's in English Literature would be fun. I also had the desire to live in England, having loved it while exploring it after spending a semester abroad in Paris.

Before college graduation, I secured an internship with Plazm Magazine, an esoteric art and culture magazine in Portland, Oregon. After the festivities of graduation were over, and what felt like sleeping for an entire week, I started planning my summer. I'd move to Hood River and learn to windsurf to win my dad's bet (if I waterstarted and sailed one hundred yards, he'd buy me an apartment). I'd commute an hour to Portland for my internship and in September, I'd move to England. This plan made my heart leap.

It only took a few weeks for me to realize that three months was hardly enough time to thoroughly enjoy my new-found freedom of living away from home in a city I loved and without the pressure of college deadlines. I wanted more of the same.

My parents were livid.

"You are not taking time off. What are you thinking? Graham didn't take time off after Penn. He went right into a combined JD/MBA at Wharton and Penn Law."

Instead of getting real life experience like most people are required to do just to qualify for applying for business school, he got right in, taking no time off between undergrad and grad school. It's not common for people to go straight from college to an MBA program. They often work in the business field for a few years to gain experience, but not Graham. He was so smart, especially when it came to standardized tests—scoring a ninety-seven percent on his LSATs alone. He secured a spot with little effort, making me feel like an idiot and even more inadequate for not getting into an Ivy League for undergrad. Not to mention, he went to the best schools in the country. Who could blame my parents for being proud of him?

But if there's one thing I learned from my family, it's the art of arguing. Even if I lost, at least I'd put up a fight.

"Mom, you're one to talk. You and your mother traveled around the world after you graduated from college." Then, I put my father in the crosshairs. "And Dad, your argument holds no weight; after Princeton, you had every intention to play baseball and did just that. The only reason you went to law school a few years later was because you felt pressure from your father to get a real job and stop playing ball.'"

Not only did they fail to back down, their subsequent calls were relentless. They were bound and determined to force me onto a plane to England if it came to that. My reasoning seemed to fall on deaf ears. This wasn't the way they wanted it to be. No doubt, they wanted to be able to tell their friends that their son had earned a JD/MBA at Wharton and Penn Law and was working at Credit Suisse in New York City and their daughter was pursuing a master's in English Literature in England. What would they say if their daughter was just enjoying herself in some podunk city where she was only interning at a little-known magazine? They were paying for the successful version of their daughter, not the one living in Cow-town.

Of course, I took their criticism as a reflection of the myriad ways I had failed to live up to their expectations.

I began avoiding their calls. At work, they tried to be crafty. One of the editors told me, "Serena, you have a phone call . . . Wally is on the phone;" "Walter wants to talk to you;" "Valerie has some questions."

I picked up only to learn that I'd been tricked. It was one of my parents still trying to force my decision.

When I told them both that they'd have to drag me onto a plane kicking and screaming, they finally caved. The battle had been won but at an enormous cost.

Sometimes I surrendered; sometimes I fought to the bitter end. Regardless, I had zero trust in my own decisions. I would defend them at all cost, even though I was never sure if I was right. I would decide to do something but would always doubt myself. I would buy something, whether big or small, and wonder if I should have bought something else. All the time I hid the shame of not completely trusting myself, and letting my parents run the show. It would take another decade for me to become more confident in listening and following through on what I wanted despite my parents' opinions.

THE SERVER COMES BY AND TELLS US ABOUT THE SPECIALS

On tonight's menu we have a delicacy. Some might say it's an acquired taste, but those who have savored this before will appreciate the offering: Pain-stuffed emotions drizzled with resentment, sadness, and frustration. This is accompanied by a bed of narcissistic personality disorder. You can get the narcissism on the side if you'd like but most people like to get as much narcissism as possible. We also have a seared lack of love that many people have said goes right to their hearts. The sides for these include self-criticism wrapped self-doubt and devilishly spiced depression smoked with anxiety. For dessert, the chef has prepared the salted caramel never-good-enough chocolate chip cookie because you'll always look for better, and the bar has a new drink called the Flatliner which makes you wonder why you were even born. Do any of these tempt you?

CLIENT CASE: MICHAEL

AT SIXTY-SEVEN YEARS OLD, MICHAEL had been retired for two years and had been struggling with pain in his low back and shoulders for twelve years. He had taken a bad fall while mountain biking and since then had felt chronic tightness in his shoulders, in particular. His physiatrist at the time told him that he had completely torn his ligaments and it would take time to feel better. But he never felt like he'd fully recovered. The stiffness caused him to have a limited range of motion and most importantly, he wasn't able to engage in the activities he loved like kayaking and canoeing. Lifting suitcases or helping out around the house also made him feel ineffective, as though he was less than a man because he couldn't lift heavy things for his wife. He wanted to enjoy his retirement rather than feel less able to enjoy his free time. Michael also mentioned that he felt depressed and guessed that, unlike his shoulder injury, it had started as far back as 1970.

He had recently come across some books about how chronic pain could be linked to difficult childhoods or emotions that were never given an outlet. Michael resonated with those ideas but after reading the books, he found the pain still there, which is when he contacted me. He figured perhaps there were feelings or events from his past he hadn't considered on his own.

During the intake, I asked Michael to feel his neck and shoulders, which he rated as an eight out of ten on a pain scale, with ten being excruciating and one being barely noticeable. Then I used muscle testing to find the emotions connected to his pain. I went through a list of feelings while testing his muscle strength and landed on the concept of his future being unclear. I asked him to tell me how he felt his future was unclear and he told me that his back and shoulder pain was becoming more noticeable. It was winter and he hadn't enjoyed the summer as much as he normally did because he couldn't take the canoe out every chance he got like he used to.

Traveling, something he used to love, had also become less frequent because of the pain he felt from sitting long hours in a car or on a plane. Years earlier, when the biking accident occurred, his medical doctor told him his injured shoulder would never be one hundred percent healthy again. Michael didn't want to take medications forever and even chiropractic and acupuncture had been temporary. He didn't know if he'd ever feel better. He felt hopeless and anxious.

I traced this feeling of his future being unclear, as well as hopelessness and anxiety, other emotions I found, back to an original event at age eight. I asked Michael to tell me how his future might have been unclear then.

When Michael was eight, his dad died in a freak factory accident. He was "doomed after that" because his mother was a "very scary" paranoid schizophrenic who was in and out of the state hospital. His father was warm, calm, and nurturing.

He provided a protective buffer to Michael's mother. He told me he never realized how severe her mental illness was until after his father died. After his death, Michael and his older sister were sent to separate foster families while his younger brother, who was still an infant, went to his aunt's house. Although this aunt took care of his brother, she never extended much love or comfort to Michael. When he visited them, he didn't feel very welcome. He had to take a few buses just to get there and he always wondered why she hadn't taken him in like she did his brother. His sister was five years older than him and as soon as she turned eighteen, she married and left the area, making Michael feel even more on his own. Michael explained that he was always embarrassed about his mother because of her severe mental illness and her odd behaviors.

When I checked for more emotions connected to this same theme of his future being unclear, and feeling hopeless and anxious, I found another age: seventeen.

When he was seventeen, Michael was in his first semester at college. To make ends meet he worked as a janitor. He had studied really hard to be admitted to college, despite no encouragement or support from his immediate family or foster family. He thought college would be the event that would put the trauma of losing his dad and dealing with his mom behind him. For the first time, he began to consider just how emotionally challenging his last nine years had been. His mother's illness and all the hardship he endured at such a young age finally caught up to him. As a result of feeling overwhelmed, he became obese because he ate his emotions. To complicate matters, Michael was anxious, couldn't speak up in class, and didn't want to discuss his family with his classmates. Instead of college being the turning point he needed to allow him to feel more hopeful, his future felt even more hopeless. He was emotionally drained and dropped out in his second semester.

Michael felt that had his dad been alive, he would have been protected from his mom, and he never would have had to fend for himself in a foster family where his foster siblings picked on him. He realized he was clinically depressed at age nineteen when he felt overwhelmed by his past as well as his future.

I asked Michael if he ever saw a therapist after his dad passed or sought help for processing all the other difficult experiences he had growing up—even if there was someone with whom he felt emotionally safe in his foster family, to whom he could communicate his feelings. He said "No," he never even considered the idea and just learned to comfort himself from a young age. I sensed that Michael had to numb any feelings of sadness about losing his dad and not having a normal mother. Whatever feelings he had of longing for love were turned off so that he could get through his circumstances.

It had been more than forty years since he had revisited his memories from childhood especially when things in his family changed so drastically. Like many people who endure traumatic events, when they recount the situation, they tend to describe the details rather than the feelings. I've found that clients often continue to look at the event objectively, from a distance. The point is to get them to consider the feelings they might have had that weren't safe to express and to validate themselves for surviving the adverse event as well as they had. Michael was no different. Even when explaining how he had to commit his mother to a mental institution for being unfit to parent, he described it matter-of-factly, as though he were explaining what he ate for dinner the night before.

I used a lot of reflective listening with Michael. After listening to his stories, I would repeat back to him the parts that he had glossed over. When I identified an emotion such as despair, I would stay there and ask him to consider what his teenage son would have felt had he been forced to go through the same experience. Often, asking clients to consider what a child, pet, or partner would have felt in the same circumstances helps them feel the gravity of what they experienced.

By looking at the emotions and events from his past that had never been discussed or processed, Michael was able to develop more compassion for himself. He was also able to give a voice to the memories and feelings that had never been examined. It was healing for him to have me hear his stories. But, for someone like Michael, who, like many of my clients, wasn't even aware of the feelings he felt about certain memories, it was healing to be able to identify and consider how those memories were still a big part of his life. I found the specific emotions by asking his body for answers using muscle testing and following the memories coming to the surface.

Michael was hard on himself. He was recently retired, married with a child, and had cultivated a good life for himself. He did that on his own. No one helped him. No one replaced his dad by being a buffer; no one protected him from his mom. He lost both parents when he was still a child. Even though his mother was still alive she was deemed incompetent by the state. He rarely validated himself for his resiliency. No wonder Michael had been depressed for so many years.

The biking accident may have been the starting point for developing pain, but the fact that his injury still plagued him twelve years later spoke more to his body holding onto emotions that had never been processed than to a structural abnormality that would never heal.

I'VE ALWAYS HAD
THE POWER

I ONLY HAD A FEW months left to enjoy Portland, Oregon before moving to Manchester to pursue a master's in English Literature. This was the summer of 2000. Summers in the Pacific Northwest, weather-wise, are perfect. Clear blue skies, temperatures in the eighties, and no humidity. They often make up for the many months of dreary and overcast skies the rest of the year.

After college, as I mentioned, I was burned out from the rigorous academics and took a year off before moving to England. I hadn't been accepted to Oxford or Cambridge but still got into two reputable schools: Durham and Manchester University. That spring, before moving to England, Graham was graduating from his law and business programs.

Even though Graham attended the University of Pennsylvania, an Ivy League school, for undergrad, it really seemed to me that I worked harder. Even college felt like a competition. There were many weekends I devoted to getting my papers written or working on my thesis rather than partying and going out. I heard of all the free time Graham had—either he was so smart he didn't need to study, or he really wasn't given as much work. Later on, I concluded that his smarts and ability to score well on tests ended there. Emotionally, he was as dumb as a sack of rocks, at least that's how his actions felt to me and my few friends who had met him. Somehow, both he and my parents would wind up turning my grad school acceptance into a sign of my moral failings, my inability to keep up with family standards.

Let's rewind the tapes . . .

Senior year of high school, I applied to thirteen colleges because I didn't really know where I wanted to go and wasn't sure where I'd get in. I had been groomed to go to a good college, one that many people recognized—certainly not a state school. My dad would even quiz me and ask me to list the eight Ivy Leagues, likely hoping I'd be admitted to one of them, having gone to Princeton himself. My mom went to Wheaton College in Massachusetts; that never fully measured up in his mind or with his family, even though she graduated Phi Beta Kappa and went on to attend business school in New York City where she was a stockbroker in a field full of men. Graham went to Middlebury but transferred to the University of Pennsylvania. When he decided to go to business and law school, he applied and was accepted to the best.

The summer before my senior year of high school, I attended a creative writing workshop at Lewis & Clark College in Portland, Oregon. I had no particular aspiration to become a writer; I had no idea at that time what I wanted to be when I grew up, but something about Oregon really appealed to me. A week there proved to be enough time to know I wanted to live in the City of Roses at some point. I applied to Lewis & Clark, where I think I would have preferred going, and Reed College, where I eventually went.

I liked that everyone seemed a little rebellious at Reed. I appreciated that the school was also known as a place for socially inept individuals. I didn't necessarily view myself as socially inept, but always felt different and preferred people who were quirky and not trying to fit into the norm. Reedies, as they were called, did the opposite of convention. They conformed to non-conformity. Some were downright weird and full-on nerds.

After graduating, I stayed on in Portland. I made new friends, lots of new friends who hadn't gone to Reed, and I found myself making up for lost time. I had a few close friends at college, but we studied so much, I didn't feel I had a good balance of non-college friends. I didn't know what it was like to date for more than a few weeks or have men show interest and ask me out. Guys at college were socially awkward and very few people dated. After college, I met musicians, thanks in part to being the music editor at Plazm Magazine (my summer internship developed into a paid gig). Many of my friends were gay men, which would be my pattern for the next ten years. We frequented a bar near my apartment and the same bartender would often serve our table. I finally got the nerve to ask him out. We exchanged numbers and then, since this predates mobiles, played phone tag for the next month and a half.

As I got to know Blake, the bartender, I found out that he was from Boston and was going back there for his brother's graduation from Harvard. Wow, I thought to myself. It wasn't that I was impressed that he had a brother who went to Harvard; it was that we already had one significant thing in common. I was due to go back to Philly to watch Graham receive his MBA from Wharton and his JD from Penn Law. We both had brothers who were high achievers graduating from Ivy League schools. Perhaps he could empathize with being the black sheep, with going against the norm and gravitating to a little-known city, as Portland was back then, while having a sibling making his parents proud.

Blake was impressed that I had graduated from Reed. He thought it was cool that I worked for a magazine and he made me feel special despite the fact I didn't feel that way about myself.

I didn't know much about Blake's brother, how many cylinders were firing for him, but my brother was doing pretty well on all fronts. Graham was dating Katherine, whom he'd met in law school. They had plans to move to New York City, where she landed a high paying job at a lucrative law firm, and where he was to begin a job at Credit Suisse as an investment advisor.

Compare that to me. I was barely dating a bartender, working at a no-name magazine, frittering away my summer, all while trying to figure out what I wanted to be when I grew up.

Mom and Dad were immensely proud of Graham, as they should have been. Me, meh. To them, I'd been goofing off after college. Yes, I planned to move to Manchester University, despite Durham being better (it still wasn't Oxford or Cambridge). I felt all of this but didn't admit it to myself because of how ashamed I felt for not living up to my parents' expectations. I didn't readily consider how much this bothered me, let alone disclose it to anyone else, especially not the hot bartender I was after. It would have been nice to find out how Blake felt about his brother, whether he felt the same pressure or whether his parents were more accepting of his choices and just wanted him to be happy. Had I known him better and felt closer to him, theoretically it would have been comforting, but I wasn't ready for this kind of vulnerability until much later.

Had I told close friends, they would have tried to assure me that I was being ridiculous and that I had just graduated from a prestigious college and was en route to attending grad school in England. It wouldn't have helped. In my mind, I was far behind where I should have been if I just applied myself more or was smart enough to get the grades for more reputable schools.

Returning to Portland, after watching Graham graduate, I developed a terrible pain in my back. I went to Lili, my massage therapist, the one who had informed me that I had an uncanny ability to use my intention to zap pain from my body, and much to my surprise, the massage gave me no relief. Next, I visited my chiropractor, Dr. Knecht, the one who introduced me to Neuro Emotional Technique (NET), which would, a few years later, with Dr. Randazzo in New York City, cure me of the chronic fatigue syndrome I suffered post 9/11. But he found nothing wrong. No subluxations. My back needed no adjustments, nor did he find any stuck emotions. Why was I feeling so much pain and not getting relief from the modalities that I had come to learn normally alleviated my discomfort?

After work one day, I decided to take a nap. Being a complete newbie to spiritual beliefs, I wasn't really sure what I was doing when I asked for insight from whatever higher power there was regarding why I was having such back pain. I snoozed for about twenty minutes and in a dream, I was sailing on the Sunfish at the family home on Cape Cod. In real life, Dad loved to take the Sunfish out, but I wasn't a strong swimmer or sailor. I always found the rough waters we often encountered rather traumatic. We couldn't have a calm and peaceful sail. We had to push the limits on the Sunfish, head to Collier Ledge—two huge boulders that jutted from Nantucket Sound—and sail right between them. Our short, relatively speaking, but tumultuous journeys almost always culminated in capsizing. My dream recalled these same outings.

"Oopsie-daisy! Serena, sit on the centerboard."

"Dad! This is not fun. Why do we always have to capsize?" I yelled at him while sitting on the centerboard to right it, then climbed on the board with trembling legs.

"That wasn't so bad, was it?" he asked, not really listening or answering my question.

At a certain point, I refused to sail with him. I never knew whether we'd have a smooth sail or not and I was tired of being traumatized. I tried to keep up. I tried to compete at his sports, the ones I felt privileged to learn, but he was always better than me. It didn't matter if it was sailing, biking, running, tennis, skiing, or any other sport, all of which he played.

Even after high school, I picked up running and he offered to run with me a few times. He'd tell Mom I had perfect form; but on the run, he'd look back and yell, "Keep your shoulders back. Keep your eyes up. Look where you're going rather than down at the ground."

Such comments reinforced the feeling of never being good enough. How was I supposed to compete with a marathon runner? Why did he expect me to learn at his knee, to become the next best thing to Jackie Joyner? He had picked up running later in life, in his early forties, because he was working too hard and feeling a little heavier than normal. Being a natural athlete, he went on to have a twenty-year running career, competing in fifteen marathons with his best time being two hours and forty-four minutes in the Philadelphia Marathon. When I asked him how he did that one in particular he told me that he had realized at mile thirteen that he'd been doing six-minute miles, so he challenged himself to see how many more he could do. I was happy if I could push myself to do eight-minute miles, but I knew I'd never achieve six-minute miles. The gap in performance was huge; I couldn't fathom bridging it. All I wanted to do was sit down and give up, take up knitting.

Graham, on the other hand, played competitive tennis. He had good form and he smashed the heck out of the ball. Dad found it fun to play Graham because he was closer to his level. Me, I couldn't have beaten Dad with Serena Williams playing backup.

So, what did my sailing dream have to do with my back? I figured something out when dreaming because when I awoke, the pain had subsided considerably. I started piecing it together. Dad was proud of Graham when it came to sports, but I felt like I was the sad girl who was born with innate athleticism, who squandered my gift away by developing arthritis. Despite my best efforts, all the classes I took, the practice time I put in, I would never be the athlete Graham was. I always seemed to pursue the goals set before me by my parents and society differently. The competition never ended, and it involved every aspect of my life: attending a prestigious college, getting a good job (they agreed to me interning at a magazine, but told me "absolutely not" to being a barista, even if it paid more than the internship), attending a good grad school, and essentially creating a reputable CV for them to show off to their friends. But I felt like I never truly reached excellence, I was always behind in some way.

It dawned on me that all the anxieties I had felt—about dating a bartender rather than a lawyer, graduating from a good school but not an Ivy League, moving to England to study but not at Oxford or Cambridge—didn't have anywhere to go so they lodged themselves in my back until I took notice and understood the connections. I was astounded. The pain had released from my back within minutes by expressing the feelings I felt ashamed to have.

Did that really happen? Maybe that was coincidence.

As soon as I started to doubt the connection, the pain came back.

OK, OK, I'll take it. Thank you!

I didn't know who I was thanking, but I was grateful for the experience and immensely appreciative of the pain going away.

CLIENT CASE: KLAUS

KLAUS CAME TO SEE ME because he was losing his hair. Clumps of hair fell out a year before I met him, which created a panic. Doctors had not been able to offer him any answers and he also had tension in his neck, back, and shoulders.

At only forty, he was very healthy, exercised, ate a balanced diet, and had been to a number of specialists to rule things out. He tried a gluten-free, anti-inflammatory diet for a number of months, took various herbs, supplements, and natural remedies, but he also wanted to find the cause so he could prevent the hair loss.

I started by assessing what was going on in his life—what he did for a living, his relationships—and tried to get a sense of the people or things that make him anxious.

He had moved to the US from Germany eight years prior and worked for a tech company as an engineer. He was doing quite well, as he had been promoted over the years. He was very serious about his work because he wanted to do well in the company to maintain his status in the US. He had also been married for a few years, and although things were amicable, I sensed there was some difficulty based on the fact that he said he wanted to be closer to her, but they argued more than he liked.

When working with people who have physical symptoms, I try to understand their way of expressing their thoughts and feelings. What I've found is those with persistent somatic symptoms tend to repress their emotions, so I like to find out whether they are aware of doing that and how they tend to cope with stress.

In the first few sessions, I was more interested in building rapport and finding the emotions that were associated with his presenting issue. As it turned out, he had a lot of anger and frustration about working so hard and not feeling appreciated for all he did at work and at home. Within the first session, I discovered the emotions of anger, grief, and depression. I shared with him how these emotions connected to what he was dealing with and why. As a result of repressing these things, his body took on the burden instead.

Anger came up when assessing the emotions closest to his conscious awareness. He explained that he was angry with his wife because she wanted a baby so badly yet couldn't get pregnant. She wanted to do fertility treatments, but he preferred to let it happen naturally and it angered him that she disagreed about how to have a baby.

Depression showed up when testing his symptoms and finding a connection to finances, which he explained had to do with developing his own business. As I dug for more information on the connection between depression and having his own business, Klaus said that he put a lot of pressure on himself for things to work out and be successful and when they were not, he got depressed. When I looked for an earlier event where he felt a similar feeling, I found his father put a lot of demands on him to be a good student and he felt like he never measured up. I helped him understand the deeper connection: he was angry at his dad for not being someone he could connect with; as a result, it was difficult to meet his needs, which caused him to internalize his feelings.

Grief was connected to a past relationship. He and his college sweetheart in Germany had a wonderful relationship. For whatever reason, they went their separate ways and he continued to mourn the loss—another example of feelings he pushed away, thinking there was nothing he could do about them. I explained that unless he found a way to express them, his body would do the work for him, and continue to create somatic symptoms.

I gave him exercises to do, including taking note of what happens when he feels frustrated. Does he tell the person how he feels? Does he make judgments or play out different scenarios in his mind with the people who irritated him, then live out the results before asking those involved for their side of the story? This is something of which we're all guilty; for Klaus, I sensed a lot of conversations were taking place in his mind about his relationship issues with his wife, without allowing her to live outside of his mind.

After five sessions, Klaus came in and explained that he noticed he was very frustrated in his marriage; but instead of having conversations with his wife, he would just get angry at her and her demands, and then decide they weren't working out. As a result, he had become distant. The more she nagged, the more annoyed he became. He said she had been pressuring him to have a baby for over a year and he didn't feel like he was ready; the more she pushed, the more he retreated, because he felt like she didn't understand him.

I asked him to tell me what he'd like to tell her, if he knew he wouldn't be judged and she wouldn't react adversely.

'I'd tell her that I work so many long hours, including travel, so I'm gone for an entire week sometimes. If we have a child, I want to be home; I want to focus on being his or her father. I don't want to be the absentee dad that has no relationship with his kid. I had that with my dad and it still bothers me. I feel like I missed out. You want a baby, but do you still want me? I feel like all we do is fight and that wouldn't be fair to a child either. We're so distant. Why don't we talk more or even laugh? I feel like I can never do good by you and you're always finding fault with me. And my hair is falling out and I don't know why. I would really like to get well before bringing a child into this world.'

He said it was liberating just to tell me—it was liberating to be so free with expressing himself; he felt lighter.

I helped Klaus process the fear regarding how his wife would react if he told her exactly how he felt. Then, I assisted him in having a discussion with her, whereby he could discuss his concerns about their relationship and plans for having a family. By the end of our treatments, his hair had stopped falling out and the pain in his neck, shoulders, and back had released.

TURNING POINT

WHEN I WAS IN LONDON earning a master's in international journalism, the pain in my body became unbearable. I didn't know if it was the fact that I felt disillusioned by journalism and that it wasn't as fulfilling and satisfying as I thought it would be, whether it was the weather in London, or the food (which is not the greatest in the world). But something was really making my body sore and stiff. It was difficult to really enjoy myself in this international city to which I had been so excited to move.

Some of my British classmates said things to me that made me upset. I wouldn't say anything to them; I wouldn't exhibit any sense of dissatisfaction with them. But I would feel hurt and angry and wonder why they were being so mean. Then I'd go on about my day.

This one guy, Scott, was a really good-looking British guy, or British bloke. He asked me questions that I wouldn't know the answer to—questions about the US and US politics. It was right after the presidential election between Al

Gore and George Bush, where it took the US a few months to figure out who had won. "What is a hanging chad?" Scott would ask. "Why do you have an election system that would allow for it to be so difficult to know who won during such an important race?"

I didn't know.

He would look at me with incredulity, and I would feel really ashamed. One day he asked me, "How can you not know the politics of your own country? That seems really bizarre." He made me feel stupid and so small.

I was so angry, and the physical pain was getting worse. As soon as I got home, I decided to start writing. I wrote about how much Scott upset me as well as how depressed I felt in a city in which I should have been so grateful to live. I wrote for about forty minutes, and when I was done, the pain was gone. You would have thought that realizing I had just unlocked this amazing superpower would have blown my mind. "Wow, with writing I can unlock physical pain that has been causing me so much harm, physically, emotional, spiritually, and mentally." But no, instead it was more like, "Hmmm, that's cool. I guess if I just write down my thoughts that I'm unable to express verbally, I can get the pain to go away."

It made me curious, so I started reading up on the subject of the mind's ability to overcome physical pain. I consumed everything I could find on the mind-body connection. It turns out this was not a new technique. I was not the first to discover this ability to undo physical pain by releasing repressed emotions. It turns out that there were a few doctors, at least at the time, who were also researching and raising awareness about this topic.

LIMITATIONS OF THE
TALKING CURE

IT WAS JOURNALISM I'D SET out to study in England, not psychology. After finishing course work in London, I moved to New York City to start working at *Spirituality & Health* magazine, but I still had to complete my thesis for journalism school. I interviewed a journalist who had hired me for a summer internship during college in New York City. Christina was someone I admired and respected. She must have seen the sadness I was trying to hide after my recent experience with 9/11 because she suggested I see a psychologist. She made me feel like it was OK to feel unhappy and pointed out that many in the city were still reeling from what had happened in their own backyard. She told me she had seen the psychologist she recommended. Talking to a professional had helped her during a difficult time. Her demeanor allowed me to feel like it was OK to get help. It wasn't a sign of weakness, as I'd been led to believe. Perhaps this psychologist, I mused, could help me get over my sadness and help me move on with life.

I never found talk therapy to be helpful, even though I hold a psychology degree.

I had my first experience with the stuff in high school. I was pretty depressed at the time yet didn't disclose to anyone just how bad I was feeling, not even to my closest friends. However, one friend, Alexandra, whose mother is a psychotherapist, could tell I wasn't doing well, and urged me to get professional help. She told me that talking to someone would make a big difference and finally convinced me to give it a try. But I was so uncomfortable with the counselor who wanted me to confide in her and tell her my deepest, most personal thoughts and feelings. It wasn't safe to be vulnerable with another person or even a professional. I would only be judged for being weak, have my emotions turned against me like my family had, or my experiences would be dismissed entirely. It was better to bottle it up and keep it to myself. I was polite to the school counselor. I told her I didn't want to be there, that it wasn't for me, and left. Ashamed for seeking help to begin with, I lasted twenty whole minutes before waltzing right out the door. "Only sick people see psychologists," was the message I got growing up. I never returned to another therapist's office until after 9/11.

Neither at school nor at home was it mentioned or encouraged to see a shrink. If I wasn't doing well at school, I sought help from a tutor and even then, I felt bad about myself, as if I wasn't smart enough to get better grades.

Did anyone in my family ever see a shrink? My great aunt Harriet likely saw a psychologist after watching her mother get decapitated in an elevator when she was a teenager. Who wouldn't need that kind of help after such trauma? I loved Aunt Harriet. She was fun and spent time with me growing up playing Candy Land. But I was always told she was crazy.

My grandmother was a child psychologist, but from what I could make out, she only treated really messed up kids—kids that run into a room kicking and screaming, kids that tear pictures off the walls and piss on the furniture. I certainly didn't want to be thought of as one of them.

The idea that high functioning adults and children could seek therapy to get help with a phase of life or with their emotions was completely foreign to me. But the stress from 9/11 made me rethink my position.

I knew I was depressed and tired of trying to make sense of the world. Since I wasn't sure what would help me feel better, I decided to see the recommended psychologist. I was still talking to Lili, getting her help, but I knew there was a difference between coaching and therapy. I needed serious help.

I arrived at the therapist's spacious apartment; we walked through her immaculate kitchen and living room—the place looked like it had come out the pages of Dwell magazine—then I sat in her office feeling awkward and uncomfortable. I guess she was cutting down on expenses by seeing people in her home, but all I saw was an image of success. I was feeling anything but successful at the time, so the power dynamics put me on guard. Here I was, about to open myself up and let this stranger see all of my vulnerabilities and weak spots. I might as well have been walking through Times Square buck naked. Why was her office in the farthest corner of her apartment, I wondered. Was the woman giving me a tour of her home so that she could demonstrate her authority? Was she going to manipulate me into telling her where and how I wasn't achieving what I wanted in life, what I lacked, so she could lord it over me? I came from a high performing family, where appearances meant everything. Looking good on the outside, even if you couldn't label a feeling to save your life, was all that mattered. Before this therapist even started the session, I had already decided I was not about to give her any ammunition to show me how much smarter or more successful she was. Her home tour had shown me all I needed to know about the situation I found myself in.

"Why don't we start with you telling me what's on your mind," she instructed.

"Well, Christina suggested I see you because of what I experienced on 9/11." I went into the facts of what I'd seen that day, never emoting, never feeling the sadness or hopelessness that encompassed my new existence. While I droned on, I kept comparing the session to the ones I had with Lili. I'd been coaching with Lili for a year, starting in Portland, continuing in London, and then New York. She was engaging. She asked questions and offered feedback. She didn't sit back, ask a question and let me vent or describe a situation for half an hour without interjecting. Lili challenged me to look at my thoughts and behaviors and make connections, which shifted my experience. Most of all, she helped me move out of my comfort zone.

When my therapy session ended, I wasn't about to let the woman know that I found her ineffective. I was polite and thanked her for the session. I thought that telling her I wouldn't be coming back because I found the past hour useless would only make her explain to me all the reasons why I was wrong and make me feel like I was the one who didn't get it. I assumed she would suggest giving it a few more sessions, but I couldn't wait to leave. I played my part as the patient and that's where the game ended.

I chalked that one particular session up to a lesson learned. Therapy might be helpful for some people, I decided, but sitting and talking to a stranger without being given concrete tools or ideas to challenge my way of thinking did nothing to help me feel better mentally, emotionally, or physically, so I concluded therapy wasn't for me.

Talk therapy reminded me of dealing with my family, people who had no interest in hearing unpopular truths. I could stay a few steps ahead of the therapist and strategize how to answer the questions. I could describe events and offer a string of details and not go into my feelings. I know it's difficult to label emotions and express how things feel and yet, therapists let me stay comfortable, never probing for why I was so detached and distanced from my emotions. My problem lived there, in my detachment. Most of what ailed me—the depression, the exhaustion, and the chronic pain—sprang from there. I cut off from my feelings at a very young age. It was safer to be in my mind, analyzing. I could explain to myself why things happened, why people were the way they were, and why I reacted the way I did as if I were a robot spewing data. My analytical nature gave me answers but it didn't help me feel much of anything.

I need someone to short circuit the robot, to interrupt the analysis, so I'm left out in the open with my feelings. Because I won't give up that survival mechanism voluntarily. That's why I have always sought alternative types of practitioners. I need to be surprised. The techniques that I find most beneficial are the ones that bypass my rational brain, which knows what to say and how to act. They get in sideways and access the unconscious, which is where the goods are stored, the feelings that I've buried for years, which felt too unacceptable or scary to feel.

Coming out of that disastrous talk therapy session, struggling with the weariness of it all, I knew I needed answers. I felt the fatigue jeopardizing my career. If I didn't complete my thesis, I'd never graduate from journalism school, and then where would I be? If I didn't perform at the magazine job I'd worked so hard to land, it would only be a matter of time before I'd get cut. Working from home only exacerbated my extreme tiredness. My sofa became my nap nook and we all know how that ends. It was time to take matters into my own hands because I was desperate to stay on track.

After my medical doctor diagnosed me with Chronic Fatigue Syndrome and told me, "There's no cure. Just learn to cope. Stay away from sugar and caffeine," I decided that I needed a stimulant, something like Adderall or Ritalin to give me the boost that no amount of caffeine could offer. When I couldn't get my hands on an Attention Deficit Disorder medication, I used cocaine. Talk therapy didn't offer any help, and even though coaching kept me focused on my goals, I still felt hopeless and hardly able to accomplish anything. When I did have feelings, they were depressing. *Why live? Why keep going if something like 9/11 can happen and terrorize an entire city and country and kill the people closest to you? What's the point? Writing for a magazine . . . where's the purpose in that?* My drive and motivation were gone. After a month of doing lines of cocaine in my kitchen to stay awake, I knew I needed a real answer. My true interest was in health and wellness—I was working for *Spirituality & Health* magazine—yet I felt like the biggest imposter.

I remembered the chiropractor Lili had introduced me to while I was still in Portland. He used something called Neuro Emotional Technique (NET), which asks the body for answers, which was precisely what I needed. I couldn't outsmart this technique or stay a few steps ahead. I knew I was stuffing my emotions and had a big hunch that my fatigue, sadness, and joint pain were connected to all the feelings I felt too vulnerable to express.

After finding an NET doctor in Manhattan and feeling a

huge difference even after the first session, I continued seeing Dr. Linda Randazzo and kept getting better and better. After a few weeks of NET, I trusted her enough to adhere to a strict diet and take the supplements and homeopathy she muscle tested to be of benefit. My health continued to improve faster than I'd imagined. My drive and ambition returned. I lost five pounds without trying because I felt better physically, mentally, and emotionally. My thoughts were more positive and I started reading books and articles on health and wellness like I had done before becoming too tired to focus. I explored museums and different areas of the city. I finished my thesis. That moment, of course, is what launched me on my journey.

I knew I wanted to learn the emotional techniques that had made such a difference for me, the ones that could pinpoint the emotions I couldn't consciously identify. Making those connections and tracing them back to an earlier time when I felt a similar emotion and processing them in the present, seemed so simple and yet it did the trick. It got me feeling better immediately. I didn't have to talk about my feelings for months or years, the ones I couldn't label or even access. But in order to learn those techniques, I would need to earn a higher degree in one of the healing arts, which included naturopathy, acupuncture, chiropractic, traditional medicine, or psychology. Since I was fascinated by the mind body connection, of how thoughts and feelings could affect the body, I chose psychology. And just like that, I set my journalism career aside and launched myself onto the healing path. Psychology—I couldn't believe I was actually going to go down that path.

HOW LONG DO YOU
NEED TO TALK TO
FEEL BETTER?

I SUPPOSE MY DISTASTE FOR talk therapy took on a life of its own during my doctoral program. As part of my degree requirement, I fulfilled one of my internships at a San Francisco hospital.

My first patient had come in under an alias because she feared her ex-boyfriend would track her down and cause even more damage than he had already done. The night before I met her, he had held her by her ankles over a balcony a few flights up then dropped her on her head. She severed her spinal cord leaving her paralyzed from T1 or T2 (high chest). Her grandmother was always in the room, often pretending to do other things, but I could tell her entire focus was on her granddaughter. I felt it, everything. All the shock, terror, grief, sadness, anger, and bewilderment. Just like I had absorbed the anguish from my fellow New Yorkers after 9/11, I was taking on the emotions I sensed this patient was feeling. How would she and her family recover from this? The day before she had full functionality; today, she was paralyzed. Her life

70

would never be the same, or so it seemed to me.

Medical doctors and nurses would file into the room while I was there, take the patient's vitals, add to her chart, and leave. From what I could tell, they weren't attached or interested in the patient's personal story. I, on the other hand, felt powerless and ill-equipped to help this patient feel any better. I wasn't prepared to work with someone who had gone through such major trauma. What on earth could I say or do to help her come to terms and feel any better about her new reality?

Another patient was a few years younger than me. She'd been in a car accident after attending a party with her friends and brother. The driver was under the influence and she was the only survivor. Waking up in the hospital, she presented with short-term amnesia. When I met with her, she was only able to be cognizant for about fifteen minutes. She would recount the story of how she left the party with her brother and two friends and the last thing she remembered was laughing and having fun in the car. Then she would look shocked, confused, and asked, "Where's my brother? Is he in the hospital too? Is he OK? Where are my friends? What happened?" She would get tired, look disorientated, and go back to talking about the party only to ask those same questions again. It was like working with someone with dementia. She returned to a few significant memories. But it was the shock of considering that her brother and friends were dead that would cause her to revert back to not knowing their fate that got me. It was too much. It was too overwhelming, so she shut off that part of her memory. Even if it was unconscious. It registered for me. And shook me to my core.

As I sat with these patients, listened to them, and tried to offer what I knew of therapy, I couldn't help but wonder how many years of talking about their feelings and describing their trauma it would take until they felt better. How long would it take the amnesic patient to get her memory back without feeling flooded with emotions? When would the patient newly paralyzed be able to feel better and adequately cope with her new life without full mobility? How many months or years would it take for these patients to no longer feel the shock and overwhelming grief of their new situations?

I was able to heal and recover from chronic fatigue and Post Traumatic Stress Disorder (PTSD) in a matter of months because NET accessed something different than what I thought was going on. I assumed that I simply didn't know how to make sense of the events of 9/11, that the associated confusion was making me tired. It turned out that NET identified some deep-seated fears that I had buried from that day. I was so worried that it would happen again that every fire truck siren or police car racing down some avenue would catapult me into what every New Yorker learned to deal with: that of hyper-vigilance. A suitcase left unattended, sitting on a sidewalk with no owner? At that time in the city's history, everything was suspect. A bomb squad would be called in to investigate.

Instead of trying to figure it out on my own and wandering down different paths that I had convinced myself were the issues, NET pinpointed my emotions with lightning speed and made sense of the current issues even when I couldn't understand them myself. NET mobilized me to feel better immediately and took off the emotional charge, which kept me in place. Had I talked to a therapist about my fatigue and depression after 9/11 I likely would have rehashed the events over and over, thereby retraumatizing myself rather than getting at the underlying feelings that had become stuck in my body, the ones causing fatigue.

During my internship at the hospital, I felt that if those

patients with whom I was asked to conduct talk therapy could be seen by a NET practitioner a few times a week, they'd likely have a better prognosis. As a twenty-eight-year-old intern whose prior experience with talk therapy was limited to two unhelpful sessions with zero outcome, who received more benefit from a technique developed by a chiropractor, that was my thought process.

When I met with my cohort at school, where we discussed patient cases and got feedback, I did everything I could to force back the tears. Two months into my internship, I broke down and explained that I felt useless and was questioning my entire decision to pursue a career in psychology. How on earth could talk therapy help someone make sense of a new reality like the ones those patients would have to learn?

My supervisor told me that in order to do the work set before me, I'd have to realize that I was offering a service. In fact, he said people specializing in acute rehab were either very emotionally detached or were really into partying. That was eye opening. To me that meant that the options were the same: detach from emotionality or feel the emotions and find an outlet to numb them, like drinking or doing drugs. Eventually, according to him, I would graduate and be paid to listen and help people make sense of their lives and assist them in resolving their issues. If I were to become personally attached and interested in their stories and lives, I'd not only be overwhelmed emotionally, but I would be ineffective professionally because I wouldn't be able to be objective. That stuck with me for a long time. It helped me strengthen my ability to detach from feeling for my clients. If that supervisor had been more empathetic, perhaps the recommendation would have been different.

I wanted to heal others, but not like that. The cost was way too high. I had already perfected this ability to avoid feeling in my own life. I wanted to right that ship, not sink it with my work. Yet it made sense, this distancing that was required to do talk therapy. The psychologist in New York City felt distant and more interested in offering me a service than truly caring about me. On one hand, I had picked the right career because I was already comfortable analyzing people, but on the other hand, telling myself not to get attached to my clients and deeply feel for them seemed antithetical to being in the helping profession. I concluded that talk therapy would never be my game.

WHEN DREW FINALLY
SHUT UP

AFTER A YEAR IN SAN Francisco, I decided it would be a big help to have a car, so I could save my back, what with all the groceries I lugged up steep hills. I suppose there were other reasons as well, not that I can remember them now.

My mom knew of my plan and found a good deal on a car in Philly, which meant I had to fly there to drive it back cross-country. I wasn't thrilled with the idea, but I didn't have a better plan. Normally I love road trips, but my graduate program operated year-round with only two-week breaks between quarters; a trip back East would take up four or five days.

I told Drew about my plans and he offered to make the trip with me. He joked, "I can't let you drive back on your own and risk the truck drivers going after you."

Drew and I had become instant friends shortly after being introduced. He had dated my friend, Andrei, back in the mid-nineties when they were both living in Nevada. When I left New York City and moved to the city where

Drew lived, Andrei figured it would be a crime for us not to join forces. From the moment we met, Drew and I were inseparable. He quickly became my BFF.

Halfway through Pennsylvania, a big state by many people's measure, I asked Drew if he wanted to take over the driving. "Oh no, honey," he said. "My license has been expired for a year. I'm here for the company."

"What?" This had to be another one of his clever lines. He had a great sense of humor and was constantly cracking jokes. "You're not going to drive at all?"

He shook his head.

"I've made this trip before," I told him, in a huff. "I could certainly make it solo again." I was annoyed because I felt somehow manipulated. I'd been hoodwinked into believing Drew would help with the driving, only to find out he was only planning to be the passenger. It sent me through the roof that he hadn't explained any of this. Did he just come along for the ride so we could visit Andrei in New York City, or to see the sights? He had to have known that I was under the assumption he'd be driving. Even my mom had made comments to him about our upcoming drive, also assuming he'd be helping out.

We got into a minor fight over the issue. And then a bird flew into the window. Drew screamed like a little girl, and I laughed. Just like that, we got over our differences.

It was non-stop chatter from there on in. Drew was constantly asking random questions. "If you had to bury a body and cover your tracks, how would you do it?" He'd tell me all the reasons why my ideas would fail and I'd be imprisoned. He created scenarios from my answers making me think deeper and consider better responses. It was difficult for me not to love him, to forgive him.

"If you had to choose between only having sex with your husband or boyfriend for the rest of your life or only love, which would you choose?" I had no idea how to answer this; love was elusive to me. It seemed love was the right answer, because when I gave it, Drew said, "Yes, right, that's correct."

When I asked him for his answer to the same question he said 'love' as well.

Finally, as we crossed through Wyoming, Drew fell fast asleep. Peace and quiet, finally. We had chatted about other topics, but my mind returned to the subject of love. It lingered there for a very long time.

Drew had seen me date a number of men my first year in San Francisco and even helped set me up with a few eligible bachelors he knew. He had listened to me chat endlessly about my hopes and desires. My dates had turned into flings at best while he had ended one long-term relationship and was already into his next. I wondered why my flings had only been just that. Would I meet someone who was better suited for me in the future? Had I just not met the right guy?

I came across some books focused on the topic of love, written by doctors in the Bay Area. Gerald Jampolsky, MD, came to mind solely because the titles of his books were so fascinating to me: *Love is Letting Go of Fear* and *Teach Only Love*. He created a clinic in Marin County called The Center for Attitudinal Healing, which helped people struggling with chronic pain and mental health issues using principles of love and forgiveness. I was interested in finding either volunteer work or an internship at his center but wasn't sure if I'd get credit at my school or how to go about doing it. All these thoughts went through my mind as Drew snoozed.

I decided to use that opportunity to ask the universe. "What do I need to do in order to heal the arthritis, what?!"

I put it out there and then let my thoughts wander. This question had never been too far from my thoughts. I thought of it weekly if not daily, even if only quickly.

Since I've always remembered how I developed and created the arthritis, I knew in my heart that I have the ability to reverse it, but I've struggled to figure out what will be the catalyst. I was able to bring the pain into my body years ago as a child, even if I wasn't aware of how powerful I was and am. Such superpower is available, but why haven't I been able to turn it on the way I did so easily when I was younger? I thought about these ideas all the time.

About forty seconds later, as I was passing a tractor-trailer, I heard one word: "LOVE." It wasn't my voice that I heard; it had come from somewhere else. I knew instinctively that the universe was answering me. I didn't know how or why, but I knew this to be the case. I asked for further clarification with a tinge of desperation. "Thank you. And what kind of love? Self-Love? Love from a romantic relationship? Hello? Please tell me more."

I listened intently for a response, but that's all I got. Sitting in that car, driving cross-country while my BFF snored, with thoughts of love and how it's all connected to healing physical pain, I wondered what would be the cure I needed to be pain-free. According to Gerald Jampolsky and other doctors, forgiveness was part of the healing equation. *Who did I need to forgive? Myself for creating pain? My brother for getting more attention? My parents for not seeing me?*

If I understood Gerald Jampolsky's books correctly, the idea of being in a romantic partnership was different than using love to heal the arthritis. When it came to the combination of love and arthritis, I sensed the connection was more tied to internalizing the anger I felt toward my parents for not seeing me or making it impossible to feel loved and attended to just for being me. I didn't know how to ask for what I wanted, which is why I went to extremes, why I pretended to have pain to finally get the attention I so craved. I had considered that the other side of anger was love and if I could learn to love myself, express my anger, and find a way to express my feelings rather than repress them, I might have a chance at reversing the arthritis.

I didn't know what it was like to be seen and heard the way I wanted, so I didn't even look for that in a partner. How would I know what to look for—or even know what I wanted—when I'd never had it before? Could I find it in a partner, whatever this magical *it* was? Was it healing love, acceptance, connection, peace, a sense of well-being? How would I even know what to look for? I mean, what variable would do the trick and allow me to heal? I didn't even know what love felt like. It was simply a nebulous concept that sounded nice. Apparently, everyone was seeking it so perhaps I should too, and that might be the healing force I needed to reverse the arthritis. But I wasn't certain.

When Drew woke up, he said, "Pull over. I've got to piss like a racehorse."

That was the summer before I met Apartment Boy.

APARTMENT BOY

I DON'T KNOW WHEN I first started noticing Apartment
Boy. I had my fill of living in the Castro, the epitome of a
gay neighborhood. A year and a half after moving to San
Francisco the place had gone nuts with the legalization of
marriage for the LGBTQ community—loud parties every
night near my apartment, people yelling on the street below,
and so on. Sure, I was pro-gay, but I wanted more balance
between homos and heteros. I didn't want to feel so out of
place, I'd had enough of that during my life.

Shortly after moving into my new apartment at the top of
Russian Hill, I noticed a man with a dog, one he appeared to
take on most errands. *That's sweet*, I thought as I noticed him
walking down the hill and then back up with dry cleaning
slung over one shoulder, the dog's leash clutched in the opposite hand. I found myself watching him with full attention.
He was tall, athletic, toned, and looked like a nice guy, but I
was too shy to even say "Hi."

Whenever we saw each other in the lobby (it seemed

we lived in the same building), we smiled at each other in greeting, but that was it. I likely smiled quickly and looked down, which was what I normally did when someone I liked showed me attention. Give me someone fat, bald, and unattractive and I'd grin like a hyena and talk to the guy like an old friend; I wouldn't have feared rejection with someone I wasn't interested in. The sweet guy with the dog, well, I treated him like a pariah.

Each morning, I'd wait outside the building for the cable car. I had figured out in which apartment my crush lived. I looked up at Apartment Boy's bay window, which had fresh flowers on the sill, and wondered if the flowers were there for his girlfriend or wife. But I never saw him with anyone besides his dog, not even friends. His dog, a German Shepherd mix, would often put her nose out the bay window, look at the people and sights below, which made me like the two of them all the more.

I had become so fixated on the man that whenever I saw him driving nearby, all other scenery would fade out of sight. I'd see the dog in his silver pickup truck, but nothing more. Trucks, the cable car, birds, and any other noise faded into the background. Soon enough, I realized he was parking the vehicle in the assigned spot next to mine.

I would tell my friends at school about Apartment Boy sightings. They saw my excitement and told me to approach him, say more than "Hi," and see where it went from there. I told them it was too intimidating. Some other scenario would have to happen in order for me to feel ready to talk to him. A shooting star, maybe, a five-alarm fire that threatened the neighborhood, a package addressed to him delivered to my door.

One evening, while walking to my car, I spotted him in

the garage. He had just parked and was gathering his things from his truck. I felt like I was in quicksand. As much as I wanted to, I could think of no reason to turn around and pretend I'd forgotten something. There he was. I wanted to run away and at the same time I wanted to meet and talk and find out about this mystery man who mesmerized me every time I saw him.

His dog trotted up to me while he continued collecting his things and I leaned down to pet her, always a safe bet. Dogs have always made me feel comfortable and the German Shepherd was no exception. My mind was racing. *Oh my God, oh my God, oh my God!* He's walking right toward me. He came over, naturally, and we started talking.

"Hi! Where are you off to?" he asked.

That was already rather personal. *Why was he interested in where I'm going? I wondered. I'm in school. I'm not going to some high-paying job. I'm working with low-functioning people for free in exchange for experience and I'm only two years into a five- or six-year program. Oh man, he's going to judge me for being a student yet living in a nice pad in Russian Hill. Why did he have to ask me this question? Well, I can't think of how to lie my way out of this. Might as well tell him where I'm going.*

"I'm going to my internship. I'm in grad school for psychology and I have one more client tonight. What about you?" I looked down at his outdoorsy gear, hiking boots, and mud splattered clothing. "Looks like you've been on a trip."

"I'm just back from a week in Tahoe. I get the summers off. I'm a third-grade teacher."

"Oh, wow. That's a really nice perk."

Was I really talking to Apartment Boy? My heart raced and I hung on his every word. I was also aware that I didn't say, "Aww" in response to his comment about teaching kids.

My friends later swooned at this tidbit when I gushed about our interaction. Me, I'm not a huge fan of kids. I didn't necessarily want him to know that about me. Strike one: we don't share the same values. Another fifteen minutes and he'd be aware of strikes two, three, four, and so on.

"You know," Apartment Boy continued, "I always see you running for the cable car or coming in when I'm going out. I'm around a lot, especially since it's summer. Would you want to go out some time?"

Was this really happening? Was this guy I'd been intrigued by for the past few months, and who I was completely attracted to on a level that felt deeper than a purely physical connection, asking me out? I couldn't believe it. I said "Yes," and we exchanged numbers. I was so flustered I could hardly keep four numbers in my head at a time let alone ten, even after asking him twice to repeat himself. I didn't want to ask a third time and risk sounding like an idiot who couldn't enter a ten-digit number into my phone. He dealt with third graders who could no doubt perform better than a twenty-seven-year-old woman. Strike two. I hoped for the best but when I got home later and looked at the number, I could tell one digit was missing. I wasn't about to let this opportunity slip away so I wrote Apartment Boy a note and slipped it under his door. "Hi, it was so great running into you earlier. In my excitement, I didn't enter your number correctly so here's mine. Looking forward to hanging out soon."

When our date came a few days later, we met in the lobby and walked to get a bite to eat followed by drinks. From the moment we started talking it felt natural, comfortable, as if we'd known each other for years. It was as though we'd been friends since we were young and were picking up after many years apart. I hadn't felt that comfortable with anyone, let alone a guy I was attracted to, since . . . well, never.

He disclosed that he'd been married before to a girl he met in college. He was hesitant to tell me, no doubt feeling like I would judge him for a failed marriage, but I didn't see it that way. The disclosure made me see him as a step ahead of me. I hadn't been in a relationship for more than a fling at that point and here he was telling me that he'd fallen in love with someone in college and married her soon after graduating. That, to me, suggested he was more grounded in himself, didn't fall prey to self-doubts the way I did; he was sure of his feelings for another person, and acted on them. In contrast, I had been having one-night stands and no real possibility of anything long-term for the past few years. I felt behind in my relationship skills.

Apartment Boy wanted to know why I changed careers and he showed interest with such curiosity that I felt comfortable revealing my reason for pursuing a degree in psychology. I shared with him my personal history of developing arthritis, which spurred my desire to better understand how the mind affects the body and the body influences the mind. For some strange reason, I didn't worry that he'd judge me. There was nothing about the way he sat and took my story in that made me feel like he'd criticize me. He showed open interest and even admiration that I was earning a degree in psychology. Much like the bartender I briefly dated in Portland the year after college, who respected me for working at an art and culture magazine, Apartment Boy appreciated my life decisions and passions. As a result, I felt like I didn't have to hide. It had been a very long time since I felt good enough, that I didn't feel compelled to defend the fact that I'd yet to earn my degree or that I had yet to figure out my life. I felt a thousand years behind—behind my brother, behind my friends, behind my parents' expectations of me—yet I was exactly where I was supposed to be when sitting with him.

Apartment Boy wasn't intimidated by my psychology training like many men I'd been out with since moving to San Francisco. Those men were afraid that I could see through them and understand their issues better than they could. With them, I felt I had to be careful with what I said or how I acted. With Apartment Boy, it was so easy and I felt so emotionally safe. I didn't feel the need to be two steps ahead of him like I normally did. I didn't have to think of what to say or what he was getting at and how then to respond. I could be myself for once and it was incredibly healing. Maybe he wasn't counting my strikes after all.

How was it possible that he was genuinely interested in me, not for what I had or didn't have? It was a common problem with me: men finding my possessions interesting but not me. I always felt nervous on a date, like I was auditioning for a role I'd never get. I learned to dread the experience. Yet with Apartment Boy, I didn't need to prove myself, or jump through hoops to earn his interest. Whenever I spoke, he leaned in, smiled, laughed in all the right places; he enjoyed our banter. Relaxed in his own skin, he didn't seem to be looking for an opportunity to cut in or one up me. It wouldn't have occurred to him. Suddenly, I could show my true self to him and enjoy being rather than doing. He saw me, Serena the young woman, not the brainy doctoral student who should be doing so much better; not the, oh, fill in all the blanks with those things I brought out—those things I hid—in situations like this.

We moved right into dating. Within a week, we were sleeping together, going on hikes, having dinners, calling each other, basically acting, and looking like we were in a relationship, all without setting a solid foundation of friendship. That was my mistake. Our physical attraction was so strong, we didn't spend time developing the emotional connection because I felt like it was already there. Relationships are not like instant pudding. I didn't know the meaning of "taking things slow." If I liked someone and there was a mutual attraction, I dove into the deep end and learned to swim afterwards. I didn't know that developing a friendship and earning each other's trust is a process, which doesn't transpire overnight. When it evolves, that's when the feelings deepen. I didn't understand this theoretically or experientially until many years later.

At the time, I had no clue how things worked. I knew flings. Those were easy because I didn't have to put my feelings on the line, risk getting hurt, and I could gain some form of validation. Once bored, I could move on. I'd grown up with parents and a brother who were emotionally unavailable. Not getting attached was second nature to me. But I didn't have experience in sleeping with someone who wanted more than a wham, bam, thank you ma'am or with someone who I liked even more outside the bedroom. I didn't want to reveal to Apartment Boy that I was clueless when it came to having a relationship. He had disclosed that he'd only slept with three women in his life: his ex-wife, a one-night stand, and me. I knew I was more than a one-night stand, but did that mean we were now in a relationship?

It was all fun and games when I could be myself; but when the doubt tapped me on the shoulder, reminding me that I didn't know what forming a relationship entailed, that's when I hoped he wouldn't catch on. I wanted him to see me as the fully capable girlfriend rather than someone who hadn't moved beyond riding a relationship bike with training wheels. I didn't know how things worked. I was used to jumping into bed early on with men but not doing the normal dating activities I associated with real couples. I'm afraid, had we taken it slowly and waited to be more physically intimate, I would have been just as baffled. There was no slow going in my dating repertoire, nor getting to know each other. There was only the quick to undress and move on in my history.

Apartment Boy was in touch with his feelings and would tell me when something bothered him. But I lacked that ability. I had learned to internalize my feelings from my family. My feelings didn't matter unless they were in agreement with my parents. I wasn't aware of this at the time. I thought the communication Apartment Boy and I had was good yet . . . Initially, we didn't set any boundaries for living in the same building. Maybe that was the kiss of death, I don't know. He knocked on my door one afternoon while I was eating lunch. In an instant, I was at the door, flinging it open with a huge grin on my face. I nearly tripped over my feet to greet him and literally flung myself at him as he walked inside. My arms were around him like a python on its prey and I wouldn't let go. It was as if I hadn't seen him for months when it had been two days. I acted like a twelve-year old girl who was excited to be asked to dance by the most popular guy in school. Should I have waited to open the door? Acted cool? He hugged back but I could feel him extricating himself from the hug while I clung to him. He asked me what I was up to. I tried to act cool and dismiss the half-eaten bowl of pasta on my kitchen table. He saw it and made his visit super short. After he left, I began to ruminate about how I had come off. The veil had been lifted. He's seen the real, damaged me. It was no longer safe to be as into him and show it.

We were being who we were, expressing the truth about how we felt, yet, maybe I shouldn't have gone with that. Maybe the truth did need a little varnishing. Later that day, he told me he felt uncomfortable; he felt like he had interrupted me, and I had put down whatever I was doing just for him. He told me that he respected and admired my independence and, in that instance, I didn't show any. He had seen me for what

I was, someone who wanted love and connection so badly, and I earned a strike for that. I felt blindsided, so ashamed of my needs. In that instant he basically told me that I was way more into him than he was into me. Not only that, I was clingy and he wanted me to know it so I could tame that, do something different, revert back to who I was before I had my tag showing. The message I got was that it wasn't OK to be myself, to be as excited to see him as I had been. As a result, my walls went up.

Apartment Boy suggested that we call or text each other rather than knock on each other's doors in order to give ourselves more boundaries. Had I been knocking on his door too much? Making assumptions?

Boundaries. I knew I didn't have them. There was nothing off limits in my house. My life belonged to my parents; there was no them and me, there was only us. Maybe he smelled my dysfunction. Maybe he knew how damaged I was, and that was a nice way of distancing himself from me. At the time, I wasn't able to discuss issues that made me feel uncomfortable, especially not with the person I was dating—not with the person I was intimate with, with whom I thought I could share it all; not with the person who would judge me as a woman, the role I was most unsure of; not with the person who I had allowed myself to be vulnerable and trusting around. I had mis-stepped, and now I had to find a way to make it OK for myself. I had to make the error his, not mine.

There was a party coming up to which it would have been great to bring him, but I didn't want him to feel like he had to go. I was worried that he would feel like I was now showing him off like women often do at weddings, only for the guy to start wondering how to untangle himself from any commitment. I hated not having the guts to invite him.

I was at his apartment one afternoon doing homework for school while he was planning homework for his students. I tried to bring up the whole "what are we doing/where is this going" conversation as nonchalantly as possible but it felt awkward. He wouldn't look me in the eyes as I asked him if we were at that stage where we went to each other's work parties. He was vague in his answers and basically told me to do what I wanted. I felt bad for bringing it up. I should have stayed quiet and let things evolve without needing to know where it was going. I should have enjoyed the ride as long as it lasted and maybe it would have lasted longer.

To cover my fear and embarrassment, I asked him if he thought we should see other people. I had met men online and off before Apartment Boy and had paused my profile as soon as he and I had become an item. But I wasn't sure about what we were doing. Everything had happened so quickly. It felt like a relationship, but we never used the words "boyfriend" and "girlfriend" and so I wondered if I was jumping the gun. Should I go back online? I didn't want to assume we were more than we were. I also didn't want him to feel like I was rushing things and make him feel pressure because that would surely cause him to bolt.

It didn't dawn on me that he may very well have seen my question as a sign our relationship wasn't working. That whatever we were doing wasn't enough and I wanted to date other men. Why couldn't I have been happy with what I had rather than trying to call it anything? Instead of being truthful and telling him how happy I was with him and how I had no interest in dating anyone else and asking for his opinion on the subject, I couched the question and made it worse for both of us. He likely took it as rejection—then I felt rejected by his dismissal of the conversation.

Things moved too quickly. I've said that a hundred times.

We went from eyeing each other, to crushing on one another for a few months, to going out and being in a relationship right away. He thought he would be married with two kids by the time he was twenty-eight, which was how old he was when we met. I didn't have a clear idea of who I would end up with by twenty-seven, let alone who I was.

It was scary to be seen for who I was rather than hiding my feelings. The problem was, even if I'd tried to hide, Apartment Boy would have seen through that façade. It's the reason I dated so many men after him that weren't skilled enough or interested in seeing beyond the wall I'd built around myself.

Ultimately, Apartment Boy wanted to move somewhere else that had more room for his dog and more access to trails than where we lived, at least that's what he said. And just like that, things unraveled and fell apart. The arthritis didn't get worse but there were no more positive changes.

Five weeks, that's how long that relationship lasted. And here I am, years later, wondering what made that relationship so special. What was different about Apartment Boy? What was it about him that made me feel so held emotionally, at least in the beginning? He was confident in who he was and wasn't trying to prove anything to me, that's probably the nub of it. He didn't judge me, and I admired and respected him, which was a rare combination. He was happy with my presence and I didn't feel the need to impress him.

I remember how my body felt when I was with him. Within the first week, I started to notice changes in my body. At one point, after coming home from a run, I was on the floor stretching when my phone rang in another room. I got to my feet with ease and realized how laborious it normally was to get from the floor to my feet. When I went to see my waxer, someone I only saw once every four to six weeks, she told me I seemed different. I was more fluid and had more ease in my body. She asked what I was doing differently and the only thing I could think of was dating Apartment Boy. She just smiled with a knowing look on her face that I didn't comprehend at the time.

I left Lili a voicemail and when we met on the phone a few days later for our coaching call she told me she was so eager to talk with me because I sounded different on my message. "How so?" the same thing I asked my waxer. "More fluid, smoother somehow. Like there was an ease and an allowing in your voice." I hadn't noticed these changes in myself. But then I got to the gym the following week and noticed that running felt easier. I didn't feel heavy, like I was pulling a bag of rocks with every step. I increased my speed and it wasn't difficult to keep up. My hands even started to look straighter and less bent. What was going on? I told Apartment Boy of my new changes and he was incredibly supportive and encouraging.

This is why I think about him. This is why I think the cure for my pain is love. Because with him, I felt loved. With him, I felt I could be myself and express how I truly felt without sugarcoating—until I couldn't any longer. Once I got sucker punched and felt as though I was being too much, showing my needs and being too into him, I had no recourse. I didn't know how to repair the damage. I was too scared to let that happen again so I reverted back to dating men I could figure out within a few minutes. I needed to build up my muscles for tolerating discomfort and being called on my actions and knowing how to communicate my feelings. My hunch is, if I can recreate this scenario and find someone like Apartment Boy with whom I'm free to be myself, to be seen for all my limitations and still be accepted (by him and myself), then I'll hold the key to healing the arthritis.

Four years after dating Apartment Boy, my neighbor Jill and I went for a hike at Fort Funston, a gorgeous walk on trails overlooking the Pacific Ocean. We had just climbed what felt like five hundred steps from the beach to the parking lot when I sat down on a bench to empty the sand from my shoes. We were talking about the latest guys we were into when I saw a guy and his dog walking up the same path. He was tall and athletic, and I was mesmerized. My neighbor kept gabbing on and on and her chatter faded into the background. My full attention was now on this dude. Did I know him? Why was I so captivated by him? And then it hit me: *Oh my God! That's Apartment Boy!* I told Jill we had to go find him, but he had already made it to his truck. We got in my car and caught up to him. We were right behind him as we made our way to the exit. Jill told me to beep my horn or flash my lights. It was too late. He got on the highway. I had long since lost his number, but what would I have said if I had stopped him when he caught my eye?

"Hey, how's it going? I just wanted to let you know that you changed my life. Hope you're doing well."

How would that have gone over?

A few years ago, I found his email address when I was headed to a conference in Sonoma. I wondered what he had been doing all these years. I sent him an email and asked if the healing effect he'd had on me was something he was aware of and whether others he'd dated had felt a similar response. He told me no, that wasn't the case. But he remembered that the arthritis got better when we were together. He told me he was married with two kids. And then he told me that he still remembered the note I slipped under his door—the one I gave him when I hadn't entered his number correctly.

CLIENT CASE: MEGAN

MEGAN WAS A RECEPTIONIST AT my clinic. Because I was trying out different ways of effectively explaining how I do what I do, I asked Megan if she'd be game for a complimentary session or two. That way, she could experience my work and give me some insight into how to describe it so potential clients might understand. When a client called, she would also be much better able to determine if the fit was right. I asked her to come up with a real problem she was having, either physical or emotional, so I could run her through my process.

When Megan came to see me, she told me she'd been dealing with a pain in her psoas for five years. She'd seen chiropractors, acupuncturists, massage therapists, a physiatrist, an integrative medical doctor and had done all the stretching she could. She had injections and been prodded and poked for all those years with no real relief. At that point, she was open to anything because she was becoming anxious that the pain would never go away.

When I began working on her, the first issue that came

up was uncertainty about her future with her boyfriend with whom she'd been living. She loved him but, deep down, she knew he wasn't the one she'd end up with. How would she tell him this? How would she communicate this relationship-ending news when living together for many people is the precursor to marriage?

She did not expect me to find the emotions connected to her uncertainty about her boyfriend by assessing the pain in her psoas; but since it was something she knew and felt and yet wasn't expressing, she understood how it could become lodged in her body. She got it. She didn't want to have that confrontation because it would mean hurting her partner and being responsible for his pain. That's what she feared. So, she was in pain, real physical pain.

We stopped there. That was a load of bricks to sit with for her first session ever.

The next week when Megan returned, she said her psoas pain had improved, much to her amazement. It hadn't budged for five years and after one short session looking at her repressed emotions about her boyfriend, she'd felt a shift. When I work with someone, the issue in the body is often just an entry point for finding what is going on in the mind that isn't being expressed.

Megan asked to continue. With each session, I found that she'd taken some major strides in assessing her relationship. By the last session, she had broken up with her boyfriend. She told me there was no point in dragging it out. Knowing he wasn't the one and realizing her difficulty in admitting this to herself had caused so much pain in her body was all the impetus she needed to call it quits.

The following week she reported that the psoas pain had miraculously evaporated.

After so many years of doctors accurately diagnosing where the pain was but being unable to alleviate it, she was ecstatic. She said her whole life had changed not just her pain. I asked her what she meant by that and she said that being in a relationship she knew didn't have a future was holding her back from moving forward professionally. She had taken the receptionist job as a way to have some stability but found it difficult to move forward. She didn't want to be a receptionist forever. After our sessions, she felt a renewed sense of drive, ambition, and confidence. She applied and was accepted to earn a degree in naturopathy.

Soon after leaving the office and attending grad school, she met The One. They're now married with a baby and she's the happiest she's been in years. She gained clarity after the psoas pain went away, which people often report. That and a lightness. Her motivation returned tenfold. She sailed through school, set up her own practice within a few years, and met and married her mate. All of this seemed to happen really naturally for her. Her life fell into place all from fixing the issue underneath the pain.

A CASE OF HIVES

ONE DAY, OUT OF THE blue, I developed hives. I had never had hives before and figured it was a stress reaction to studying statistics, since that's when I first noticed them. It was my second year of my psychology doctoral program and all the courses were dry and dense. My fellow students and I concurred that the school hooked us the first year by presenting us with really engaging material so that by the time we were forced to learn courses like statistics and assessments we'd already be on board with finishing the degree.

But the hives started appearing at other seemingly random times. They were all over my body on New Year's Day when I panicked and went to the Emergency Room. My modesty went out the window, and in my gown, the type that never closes in the back, I practically stripped in front of the doctor to point out all the hives. I wanted someone to fix it. I was given Benadryl and told to take it at night, as it would make me drowsy. The only thing it did for me was wake me up in a pool of sweat. The hives didn't go away.

After coming home from a date with a guy several weeks later, I felt my lips starting to swell. I went to the bathroom and looked in the mirror.

"What in God's name is this new hell?" My lips were twice their normal size. Although I was thankful the swelling had happened after the date, this was a new symptom I now had to contend with.

The big problem was that I had no idea why the hives were happening.

On one particularly bad night in which they showed up all over my body, I ran into a friend. He took one look at me and asked, "Honey, what's going on? I didn't even recognize you. Are you OK?"

I didn't know what to say so I tried to end the conversation as quickly as it had started.

I was so overwhelmed with what my body was doing that I could hardly sleep. I waited until 5 a.m. to call my doctor, Dr. Randazzo, in New York, the one who had cured me of chronic fatigue within weeks. I cried to her on the phone, something she wasn't used to experiencing because, at that time in my life, I still kept my feelings close. She knew something was really wrong. She advised me to adhere to a really strict diet and add a lot of greens and chlorophyll to see if that would clear it up. It didn't.

I went to an acupuncturist, a Chinese lady who spoke very little English. She showed me a giant dead beetle and asked if it scared me.

"Um, yeah, it freaking scares me. What am I supposed to do with that? Eat it?"

Not exactly. I was to boil the dead beetles along with things that looked as though I had gone on a scavenger hunt for twigs and berries. I boiled that disgusting concoction for forty-five minutes and then drank the liquid. I felt calmer but the hives had not fully subsided and it was going on six weeks.

I found a practitioner, Connie Prodromou, who used energetic therapies as well as acupuncture. One of the modalities Connie used was something Dr. Randazzo had told me she was learning too, Neuro Modulation Technique. I decided to try it. Fortunately, I really liked Connie. She was like the warm, nurturing mother who wanted the best for me. After three treatments, I was all better.

What I learned was that every time I was critical of myself, my body would retaliate with hives. Connie informed me that the skin is very connected to emotions. When people are embarrassed, they blush. When you think of someone who's angry, you think of someone with closed fists, tensing their shoulders, face screwed up and red.

I kicked myself listening to Connie's explanation. How had I not made the connection?

That same semester, in one of my more interesting classes, I was assigned a Consciousness Study. For at least five days, we were told to have our phone alarms go off at random times. We were to ask someone else to program our phones so that we would be surprised when the alarms sounded. When the alarms went off, we were to take note of three things: What we were doing, what we were thinking, and how we were feeling, both physically and emotionally.

Within a few days, I noticed a pattern. Every time my alarm went off, I was aware of rehashing something that had just happened or imagining the future. I was never in the present moment. More importantly, I became aware that the things I was thinking were incredibly critical and mean. *You look fat today. You have a fat face. You're ugly. No wonder you don't have a boyfriend.* I thought all those things and more while looking in the mirror and getting ready for school; then I would close the door to my apartment and go about my day.

Now, this was in the same semester that I had developed hives so when Connie started asking me questions and explaining that the skin is often connected to anger, I was able to connect the dots.

A week went by and I had some doubts. I wanted to see if my body had healed from the self-inflicted wounds enough for me to be a little critical. I hurled some attacks and much to my amazement, hives burst onto my stomach. I learned to trust the process.

The Consciousness Study was incredibly useful for me to see where I was focusing my thoughts and how I was feeling as a result—much like Cognitive Behavioral Therapy, which posits to help people understand the erroneous thoughts they're making up about situations and then reframe those thoughts more positively to allow people to disengage from the cycle of negative thinking. I often give this exercise to my clients to help them see the connections between what they're thinking and how they're feeling.

THAT MD, NATHAN

I WAS GETTING CLOSER TO winning one of Dad's bets (the one where he promised to buy me an apartment if I could waterstart and sail one hundred yards). It didn't take long for me to realize that living in San Francisco for grad school had an added benefit: it was a mecca for windsurfing. Soon after moving there, I decided to push forward with the sport. It was no longer about winning the apartment, but learning to waterstart. Somewhere deep down, I suspected Dad wouldn't come through on it, but I pressed on in order to prove to myself first, and to him second, that I could beat him at his own game.

Rebecca and Jane were a windsurfing couple who ran a windsurfing and kitesurfing school that offered lessons and rentals in the Bay Area. Each year they hosted a clinic in Baja. I decided I'd go for six days and really commit to waterstarting, plus it would be a nice break from grad school. My mom very nicely offered to pay for the trip, and I could tell she wanted to support me with my bet. I decided to invite her along.

Like many times before, and many times after, she wasn't

as helpful as I would have liked. Neither of us speak Spanish and yet I somehow managed to drive us to our destination without any problem. My intuition told me to roll down my window when I questioned whether we were going in the right direction and ask a person who appeared to be a drunk. He enthusiastically waved us in the right direction and Mom thought this was hysterical and incredible that I knew to ask him just at the point on our trip when we could have missed our turn. Her admiration felt good.

As soon as we arrived, I was greeted by eight men, all good looking, and all really outgoing and funny. I immediately regretted my decision to have Mom in tow. Having your mom along just isn't sexy in most people's books.

Later that evening, there was a group dinner that included the men I had met earlier and a few more people. Besides the instructors and people closer to Mom's age, I was the only windsurfer. All the guys and the few women among them were kiters. Kitesurfing appeals more to young people. It's less cumbersome, equipment-wise, easier to learn, and to some, looks cooler.

As we took our seats, Mom practically pushed me into a chair right across from a guy I hadn't yet met. Nathan, I learned, was in residency for gynecology. A male gynecologist? I have literally walked out of a Planned Parenthood clinic when I learned that the hot, male gynecologist would be doing my exam.

Despite my reluctance, I found Nathan to be really down to earth, not the typical narcissist I'd come to associate with the medical doctor title. There have definitely been some exceptions to the rule. My rheumatologist, who diagnosed me at nine years old and treated me until I refused further intervention at fourteen, seemed genuinely caring and not into his title or status. The old rheumatologist nearing retirement, whom I had met with once shortly after moving to San Francisco, verged on inappropriate when he told me he found me attractive. I didn't know how to respond. I figured he was simply old school. I imagined he had entered the medical profession because he truly wanted to help people rather than feel omnipotent, make a good paycheck, and tell everyone who'd listen about his title. So, there were some "good" doctors out there, just few and far between.

Nathan seemed open minded when it came to health and wellness. We discussed our interests in our respective fields, what attracted us to pursuing our degrees. I explained my particular niche of mind/body psychology to which he responded that he completely agreed with topics like the placebo effect and psychosomatic medicine. He asked me questions about myself. He didn't boast about being a medical doctor. He talked about how most men, much like the ones at the other end of the table, simply didn't know how to relate to him because of his specialty, thereby justifying that he was focusing on gynecology because he truly cared about women's health. We talked about our training and how working with low functioning people for little to no money in exchange for experience was not always fulfilling nor did it feel boast-worthy, especially when our friends were making nice salaries in other careers. He was easy to talk to and seemed genuinely interested in me.

Medical doctors see the arthritis. There's no hiding it. They see it in my hands where it's most visible and despite my issues with most MDs, I assume they must have been trained not to ask about someone's condition until given the green light. I could tell that Nathan noticed by the way he looked at my hands for longer than normal, but he didn't ask about them.

When he asked why I was so focused on windsurfing, I explained my dad's bet and told him indirectly about the arthritis. I recounted the story of why my dad made me the bet: I'd been a smartass at my cousin, Polly's wedding at our family home on Cape Cod the summer before my senior year of college. I asked my dad why, after twenty years of windsurfing, he couldn't waterstart despite being a natural athlete in other sports. Waterstarting, you see, is a maneuver that gets you from the water onto the board without uphauling the sail; it's a necessary skill to have in order to graduate on to learning more advanced tricks. Exasperated, Dad told me that if I could waterstart, he'd buy me an apartment anywhere in the world, thinking I'd likely never even try. I informed Nathan that when someone believes I can't do something because of my physical limitations I like to prove them wrong, which is what fueled my drive toward winning the bet.

Nathan asked Mom about herself, too, and showed interest in her life. She fell in love with him in that she wanted him for me. Anyone who shows her interest and gets to know her is golden as far as she's concerned. And let's not forget, he was a medical doctor, the most boast-worthy profession as far as my mother is concerned. Regardless, it was so rare to feel heard and seen for who I really was, not how others would like me to be, that Nathan's attention felt very comforting.

And then I did it. A few days into the trip, I waterstarted and Mom was there to witness it. It felt so easy, yet not so easy to replicate. I came off the water elated. I'd accomplished what I'd set out to accomplish and met some wonderful people as well. The elation turned out to be short-lived.

On the return drive from La Ventana to the airport, a three-hour drive, I grew tired and frustrated with the conversation Mom and I were having. Mom gushed that Nathan was just the nicest young man who was so smart; he and I would make a wonderful couple.

Mom has a habit of learning tidbits about a person's life—things that have been shared with other people—yet she makes it sound as though they confided in her because she's special and so easy to talk to.

"I can't believe Nathan had a wife who left him while he was in med school. She sounds awful. Good thing you understand the amount of work it takes to get a higher degree."

This, she thought, would be the tie that bound two disparate people together. Mom kept gushing on and on about Nathan this and Nathan that and how we were destined to end up together.

"Mom! Nathan and I are friends. He's in residency in Salt Lake City. I'm in grad school in San Francisco. We have no plans to ride off into the sunset and I don't know why you think otherwise."

Mom looked down and I could tell she didn't agree with me. She wasn't going to stop because she was certain I was wrong and needed to pursue this guy. "You should really just stay in contact with him. You never know what will happen. Nothing ventured, nothing gained!" she said.

In response, I gripped the wheel tighter until my knuckles turned white. My hands hurt so much by the time we got to the airport. They hadn't bothered me on the trip there, so I deduced their pain stemmed from my conversation with Mom.

I agreed that he was very nice, no argument there. But I wasn't inclined to throw myself at the man, the way my mom was insisting I do; the reality was, we were at completely different stations in life—his station being much higher. He already had his degree, one that it seemed Mom and society viewed as better than the one I was still pursuing. Yes, he was a good guy: smart, attractive, and kind. We even lived on the same side of the country, which would, in my mother's mind, make the relationship a no-brainer. (We actually lived hours from each other, in different cities, but try getting that minor point across.) And yet, I didn't feel like I would have known how to navigate dating someone like him. It would have been nice, but I lacked the confidence. It was all fun and games when we were in Mexico, enjoying the commonality of learning a watersport, but it felt like a whole different playing field without that shared interest. I didn't want to risk the rejection, which I would have decided was about my looks, my intellect, and not being good enough. While my mother yammered on, I kept my thoughts to myself. I was annoyed but trying to remain composed and polite so she wouldn't feel upset.

When I offered up the logistical difficulties, Mom reminded me that Dad and I could go skiing in Alta and I could meet up with him there. Salt Lake City and San Francisco were only a few hours plane ride apart.

Much like other times when she tried controlling the situation and putting her stamp on my life, I felt she meant well, but that I was being suffocated. I couldn't tell her to shut the fuck up and mind her own business, that if things were going to work with Nathan then it would happen. If not, we either weren't right for each other or it wasn't the right timing. You couldn't tell her any of that because she had made up her mind that he was a catch and I should do everything possible to land him. She listened to my input but didn't hear me.

Dad's terms for our bet were that I couldn't just waterstart and then fall in the water. I needed to waterstart and keep going for at least one hundred yards. Ever the attorney, he wanted to see me do it on video or have affidavits from three witnesses as proof I'd accomplished the goal.

For Christmas that year, I let Layla, Graham's new wife, in on the gift I was giving him: a framed affidavit from three witnesses, one of whom was Mom. When it came time to open the present, he seemed to think he was opening either a framed photo of me, the two of us together, or something else of interest. Layla caught it all on camera; the look on his face when he figured out what it was. All he did was shrug, throw up his hands, and move on to the next present. I knew then that he was never going to come through on his end of the bargain.

Intellectually, I knew from years of experience that if something didn't involve or interest him, he didn't pay it much attention. Still, it hurt me that he was going to completely ignore my accomplishment, not just renege on the deal.

Deep down, what I truly wanted was his acceptance. I even wanted him to be impressed. *Wow, Serena! I never thought you could do this, especially since I can't do it. I can't believe you proved me wrong. Even given the arthritis, you powered through. This is unbelievable.* That would have been so nice to hear but I never got anything close.

Similar to the time he made me another sports bet (if I beat him in tennis, he'd buy me a car. While I got close, he defeated me seven to five in a tiebreaker and I threw in the towel. I quit playing in high school and never looked back), I only windsurfed a few more years after this bet. When you compete to win acceptance and you don't get it, those activities cease to be fun at all. You stop trusting people, too. You stop believing that people who give you their word will actually come through on it.

What hurt even more, however, happened a year and a half later, when Dad met Layla's family and they asked him about the bet . . .

Sitting around a dining table, one of Layla's uncle's asked my dad, "So were you being really generous or did you feel like windsurfing was a sport she should take up and unless you made her this outrageous bet, she'd never do it?"

"No, that's not it," my Dad replied. "I'm a really good athlete and I can't waterstart, so I figured what were the chances Serena would ever be able to do it? I mean, she has arthritis so, I was pretty sure she'd never do it."

Yep, that was Dad. He believed I would fail at the bet he made me. I sensed this but hearing him say it made it that much more real. He wasn't making the bet because he was generous or wanted me to learn a sport he enjoyed. He made it because he thought he was safe and would never need to cough up a dime. He was confident he would continue to be better at this sport even if he couldn't even do the skill he asked me to do. I won the bet, but he didn't want to admit it.

I thought back to the last ski trip my dad and I took together a few years before. We were scheduled to ski for four days, but after the first day, my feet bothered me. Even though my boots were stretched even more than they had been to accommodate my big bunions, nothing seemed to help. At the time, I really didn't suspect the pain could be anything besides the boots.

Intermediate blue squares were OK, but Dad didn't think I was challenging myself skiing them. He pressured me to ski the black diamonds even though I didn't think I was skilled enough for the steep slopes, not to mention the impact from the moguls didn't feel great on my stiff knees. We were staring down a precipice and I was contemplating how best to traverse the slope. Apparently, I was taking too much time. Dad, being impatient, said, "I get it, you have arthritis. Get over it. You're here skiing. Let's ski."

In retrospect, I wish I would have replied with something equally hurtful, but instead I sucked it up, as was customary for me, and let it affect me emotionally without letting it show, without letting him know how it hurt me. I also tried skiing through the pain from my boots but didn't enjoy it.

Back in Philly, over Christmas, Graham decided to provoke a friendly argument with Dad around the bet he made with me. Dad tried to say there was never any written contract between us, nor were the terms ever fully decided. Graham pressured him into admitting that he knew very well that he had made a verbal contract with me and that various people knew about it in the family, including my cousin, Polly, also a defense attorney.

"OK, OK," Dad said, laughing. He made it seem like this was all a joke.

Graham took offense to this and told him, "Dad, Serena spent time and money taking lessons and working to win the bet and she won fair and square. You can't just rescind the prize because you aren't happy she won. You shouldn't have made the bet if you didn't want to come through on your end."

Graham wasn't about to let Dad's betrayal go. Graham saw his actions as evidence for how Dad could do something similar to him, dangle some big prize and then take it away. People were ganging up on Dad and I was completely surprised. For the first time in what felt like forever, someone was taking my side and standing up for me. I knew Graham was arguing his point too, but it still felt comforting to know I wouldn't have to fight this battle completely alone.

The whole Baja exercise—meeting Nathan and having Mom on my back about him, learning to waterstart to prove to my father I could do it—was a complete and utter waste of time, an exercise in futility.

My hands still hurt when I think about it.

CLIENT CASE: ETHAN

ETHAN WAS AN ATTRACTIVE AND athletic sixty-five-year-old who sought my help when he developed intense pain in his right shoulder out of the blue. It caused so much discomfort that he was unable to get a solid night's sleep for two weeks; at best, he slept two hours a night. His handwriting even suffered. He was frustrated and had already seen a physical therapist who suggested his shoulder pain was due to a pinched nerve. He had also seen a chiropractor, acupuncturist, massage therapist, and medical doctor, all of whom gave him various reasons for his pain, but none were able to alleviate his symptoms.

I started the exam by asking him to focus on the pain he felt in his shoulder and muscle tested to find out what category of life his body was responding to. The most common categories are money, love, or the various roles a person plays. For Ethan, I found his shoulder pain somehow connected to the category of love. Love can be related to a person's family of origin, such as parents or siblings. It can also be connected to the self-created family, which includes friends, colleagues, neighbors, or anyone else not related by blood.

I found Ethan sensitive to his neighbor, Jack, who was having issues with romantic relationships. When someone is sensitive to another person's emotions, it's normally due to the fact that it's easier to see and understand someone else's issues before that person can see it in themselves. Ethan explained that Jack was having a fling with one woman in another state while also looking for someone within his own city, but not really committing to anyone in particular. When I asked Ethan why he was bothered by Jack's behavior (because if he wasn't upset then it wouldn't have shown up in my testing), he responded that he felt conflicted about relationships, that he didn't know how to be in one and as a result, he felt like a failure.

I continued to ask his body for answers using muscle testing and found other emotions. I found that his body also responded to the concept of time and the feeling of profoundly deep unrequited love. When I asked him to explain how he made sense of those two things he explained that he had failed to have a relationship that lasted; instead of focusing on that, he kept himself so busy that he didn't have time for one. He knew that he was avoiding the risk of having another relationship go south. He also knew that he was canceling out any possibility of experiencing love.

We traced his current conflict back to when he was twenty and felt as though he was inadequate and unable to meet the needs of his girlfriend, which made him feel like a loser. He questioned why he would pursue enduring relationships if they only wound up ending badly. After sitting with those thoughts and memories, he told me that one week before the shoulder pain started, his co-worker wanted to set him up with her mother. He thought, "Why get involved with anyone if it will eventually fall apart?" Instead of telling his co-worker that he wasn't comfortable being set up or talking to her mother, he told her that he didn't have the time. He hoped the topic would go away and he could get out of it. The set-up made him uncomfortable, but he wanted to keep the peace and not make anyone else upset so he laughed it off and went about his life. But his body became tense and developed pain because his desire for love and being in a relationship was tied up in old scripts and messages about failing in relationships. Once that was released, the pain went away.

Thrilled with the results, Ethan decided to work on other symptoms. He wanted help with his voice, a tight throat, and a general sense of being unfulfilled with his work. All of his issues however, had their roots in love, of not feeling good enough, of thinking it's better to keep his emotions in rather than let them out.

Much of what he learned about staying in control and not showing how he truly felt stemmed from his parents' divorce. His parents split when he was in fourth grade and his dad told him, "Men don't cry." As a result, he didn't cry for twenty years. He also didn't ask for help when he needed it. He learned that asking for help was a sign of vulnerability which made him feel weak and incompetent. He watched his mother breakdown many times after the divorce and he didn't want to bother her with his problems, so he kept things to himself, which became his pattern for many years.

Confrontation became synonymous with being out of control. As the "man of the house" after his parents divorced, in a family with four older sisters, Ethan learned to keep his feelings to himself in order to make others happy. His mom didn't take the split well, especially since it wasn't mutual, so she numbed her feelings with alcohol. When he and his sisters moved out of the house with his mom, he ended up sharing a room at his aunt's house with his mom who would often cry herself to sleep. He wanted to be there for her but at ten years old, he was completely ill equipped. He definitely didn't want to make her more upset by crying or complaining so he learned to shut off his needs. That was his way of staying happy even if on the inside he was anything but. He had been given certain messages growing up and would do whatever he could to create some semblance of homeostasis.

Working together on his voice and his throat tightening, we identified Ethan's inability to say something he felt he couldn't. Aggression was an emotion I found, which was related to him wanting to confront his colleague about slacking off but not knowing how; instead, he kept his sentiments to himself. I found an earlier time in his life when something similar happened. When he was twenty-seven, he felt completely unbalanced with his girlfriend. He felt like she was smarter and every time difficulties arose he kept quiet in order to keep the relationship going rather than risk having it end. Another time, I traced a similar feeling back to his late thirties when he was getting ready to tie the knot. He wasn't one hundred percent confident she was The One but instead of voicing his concerns, he hoped for the best. His intuition was communicating to him, but he chose to silence it. To express those fears would jeopardize a long-lasting relationship, which is what he desired above all else.

Like many of my clients, Ethan was very hard on himself. He was constantly criticizing himself for not being more successful at his age, not finding his passion until later in life, and even then, not excelling at it the way other people in his industry had. His significant relationships included one failed marriage, which he saw as a sign that he wasn't capable of being in a lasting one. Ethan had lost trust in himself to pursue another relationship because he felt so defeated given his history. He also knew that his tendency was to be obsessed once he started seeing a new woman and he didn't know how to have the balance he wanted.

All those fears and doubts about relationships, the pressure to live up to his own expectations in life, to be successful and make a relationship last were anxieties he didn't want to face when his colleague excitedly suggested setting him up with her mom. Just like he learned to keep people happy by not telling his family how he really felt or getting his needs met, he shut down and didn't directly answer the colleague. He got out of the set-up by being passive and nice, but his body felt all the uneasiness he didn't want to feel.

MEETING THE ANGEL
DISGUISED AS A MAN

I WENT TO BAJA, MEXICO to take a mini break from school and to try and enjoy the sport of windsurfing . . .

An added plus to being a windsurfer was that I could keep connected to Zack (a.k.a. Hot Windsurfer), someone I'd met a year after Apartment Boy. Even though I broke up with Zack eight months prior, I knew that if I asked him windsurfing questions, he would always respond. I still wasn't over him. The breadcrumbs he offered, the very reason I broke up with him, starving for a real relationship as I was, were tantalizing enough to keep me engaged with the idea of interacting with him. Zack had taught himself to waterstart in two weeks whereas I had been working at it for a few years. At his semi-pro level, he was always happy to offer advice when I asked.

During my layover in Los Angeles on my trip back from Baja, my flight was delayed. A short, older man in his sixties started talking to me as we waited in line at the ticket counter. In the span of ten minutes, he told me about his relationship, about how he felt he had not been successful in relationships until he met his wife. With her, things were easy, and they enjoyed each other as friends and partners. He described how even tennis felt more magical when he played with her because he felt so connected to her. I could feel my heart beat faster, the way it did when I found myself wanting something badly.

He asked me about my relationship, and I explained that I wasn't with anyone but had been, that it hadn't worked out. I concluded that I didn't feel I was successful at all in relationships. Although Apartment Boy had been a game-changer in that I'd seen a change in my physiology by being with him, when I had met Zack, I fell hard. Not to mention, when I met him, I had just finished a course on synchronicity, which Carl Jung referred to as a meaningful coincidence that is acausal, meaning no one could have caused it to happen. The fact that Zack's dad was a rheumatologist was all it took for me to decide it was meant to be—until it wasn't, when I found myself pursuing him. Since Zack played hard to get, I vowed that I would never feel like I was the one chasing after another again.

This man then told me, as if reading my tarot cards, that it would happen for me, having a relationship like his, but later in life, when I'm older, just like it had played out for him. "And when it does," he said, "you'll know and it will be stable, build confidence, and you'll be equals."

"But how much older?" I asked. I was twenty-nine and wanted to meet someone in the next year or so. He told me he had been in his forties, though he didn't seem to put much emphasis on his age, glossing over the details when pressed.

I thought about that and turned away to look down the terminal. When I turned back to reply, no less than five seconds later, he was gone. Poof! I looked in every direction then focused on each area of my vision more intently. Still, I couldn't find him at all. How could someone vanish like that? I looked for him on my flight and at baggage claim and there was no trace of him. Had I hallucinated him or was he an angel sent to deliver that message?

CLIENT CASE: PAUL

PAUL DEVELOPED A PAIN IN his hamstring from an injury he sustained playing soccer. He sought the help of a physical therapist to help him rehab. After six months, Paul returned to his sport, but re-injured the same area after two weeks. Once again, he began the rehab process. After another four months of physical therapy, he felt well enough to play, and was cleared by his physical therapist. In no time flat, Paul injured himself again in the same area. Three injuries in the same exact location. Something had to be up.

He went to his medical doctor who took some x-rays and an MRI; much to Paul's surprise nothing was out of the norm. While he had pain, this time there was no underlying cause. He was told to go back to physical therapy once again. But Paul knew he needed something else.

Six months later, I sat across from Paul. Using muscle testing, I assessed his hamstring to determine if there was an emotional connection and there was. Testing his muscle again, I found that the pain was connected to the category of love and when I narrowed it down even further, I had him consider the people in his life such as friends and family. I pinpointed that his mind and body were reacting to the idea of his girlfriend since his muscle tested weak when I asked him to think of her. Next, I identified emotions such as resentment, cutting off from thoughts and feelings, and frustration. When I asked him to describe how he felt those feelings in connection to his girlfriend, he said that his relationship was good but disclosed that he sometimes had doubts about the longevity of it.

I soon had a hunch what was probably at play. I sensed that Paul's doubts about the relationship were being repressed since he was so reticent to admit that he even had any doubts.

I asked him to go through the chronology of when he sustained his first, second, and third injuries. We discussed whether there was anything that was different in his life around the time of his first injury. He drew a blank, so I offered him some ideas. "Did you get a promotion at work? Did you get news about a family member, good or bad? Were any of your friends going through a tough time? What was going on with your relationship?"

A month after sustaining his first injury, he and his girlfriend had moved in together. They had been living with each other for a year while he dealt with his hamstring and lack of recovery. Since I was suspicious about his thoughts and feelings about his girlfriend, I decided to focus my inquiries there.

He had been with his girlfriend for two years before she suggested moving in together. It was her idea and he went along with the plan never realizing that it might lead to marriage, like she envisioned. He enjoyed spending time with her and although there were some things that bothered him about the relationship, like always being the one to make decisions about where to eat or what to do on the weekends, he was basically satisfied. Except, he really wasn't. She wanted more of his time than he was comfortable giving.

Paul described himself as being more introverted and desiring more time to himself to recharge. He questioned whether this was a sign that they weren't well-matched. If he was really into his girlfriend then wouldn't he want to spend more time with her rather than carving out time apart? Other issues made him question whether she was The One. He didn't feel challenged by her. She didn't offer differing opinions. Sure, she was fun to talk to and they got along well, traveled well together, rarely had fights, and yet, he felt they were more compatible as friends. But he wasn't certain either way. He didn't know whether it was better to try to develop deeper feelings for her before calling the relationship off or to realize things weren't going to change and call it quits. He knew she felt more for him than he felt for her and he kept waiting for the feelings to develop but they never did. Throughout our sessions, Paul constantly asked questions about his inability to feel. Maybe there was something wrong with him rather than with the relationship.

Every few months, the girlfriend would have a talk with Paul about their future. They were both in their early thirties and she seemed to believe they had a good thing going and the next obvious step would be to seal the deal and get married. Paul dragged his feet, told her he wanted to be completely certain he was ready to make such a commitment and needed more time. For two more years, Paul stalled the relationship. He felt he was being honest with her, but the very person he felt closest to was the person he couldn't be completely truthful with. He was scared to tell her he simply didn't have the same feelings for her despite hoping something would shift. The last two times they had serious discussions about the future of their relationship, it coincided with his second and third injuries to the same area of his hamstring.

Like a lot of people with these types of pain conditions, Paul was very empathetic. He could feel the emotions of the people around him so much that he would do anything not to hurt them. Paul knew his girlfriend would be devastated if he ended the relationship, so he made his lack of feelings for her his problem instead of accepting the possibility that they weren't meant to be together romantically. His body was communicating to him loud and clear, but he wasn't listening to the underlying cause. He kept trying to force himself to feel for her and somehow save the relationship.

When Paul wondered if he should just accept his girlfriend and decide that he'd never feel more for another, I inquired about his previous romantic relationships. There had been a few. One lasted three years, but it had been a different time in his life: he was in college. In that relationship he cared a lot about his girlfriend, but because she suffered from depression, he felt she depended on him too much and the dynamic became lopsided. He had essentially been her caretaker. Paul felt like the other woman for whom he had feelings didn't count because she was more of a fling. With her, the feelings came on fast, they were intense, and she was a challenge; he didn't know if she was as into him as he was into her. It didn't last long, but he thought of her as the second woman with whom he could access his feelings.

Using those two women, I established that he had the ability to develop and maintain feelings in a relationship. It suggested that he knew how to feel. He just didn't feel for his current girlfriend.

When he accepted the idea that they simply weren't

meant for each other romantically, he reported that the pain in his hamstring resolved within days. His fear of hurting his girlfriend and doubting his decision to break up with her had kept him stuck, but suddenly he sensed that he could be free. Once he broke up with her, the pain in his hamstring decreased even more. And when they finally moved out of their home and went their separate ways, the pain vanished.

GREG AND HIS
UNDIAGNOSABLE
PAIN

I MET GREG ON MATCH.COM while I was finishing up my predoc in San Francisco. I had plans to move to Portland in September; I was intentionally looking for men in Portland, and there was Greg. When I looked more closely at his profile, however, I was completely turned off by what I saw. "I can't wait to have that five-bedroom house in Laurelhurst with my wife and two kids," he wrote in response to one of the website prompts. Laurelhurst was one of the more affluent areas of Portland. I took this as an indication that he was just another narcissistic medical doctor hung up on image and the amount of money he made. Ugh! There was something about me and narcissists. I could spot one pretty well, yet I'd still end up involved with him or her in some way.

I was fed up with listening to men talk about themselves ad nauseam and then give no consideration to anything I had to say, yet I still attracted them like flies to a pile of shit. It's like I walked around with an antenna sticking out of my head or a sign with an arrow pointing to me that said, "All narcissists come here." The doctor thing was a bugger for me, too. Mom was, as I've said, impressed with medical doctors. So of course, I wanted nothing to do with one. If she thought they were one of two professions worthy of marriage, that was the last thing I was going for.

I was about to click to the next profile when one of his short answers caught my eye. In response to the question: *What do you do?* he wrote, "I used to be a pain doctor, but now I have pain myself. Kind of a long story; better told over a glass of wine."

Like a moth to a flame, I was drawn in. Every doctor I had met, either personally or professionally, lacked the personal experience of living with the condition they were treating. They knew the theory behind it, all the conventional treatments, but they hadn't the faintest clue what it felt like when nothing actually worked. *What kind of doctor was he?* I wondered. *An orthopedic doctor? A physiatrist? A spine doctor? How might this guy be different?* Here was a medical doctor with pain. I wanted to know more; I wanted to see if there was anything unique about him in comparison to the medical doctors I dealt with since childhood.

I've had a long history of going to doctors and not liking the way they spoke to me, like I was an object with no feelings. Or worse, they talked over my head with jargon only other medical professionals actually understood. I abhorred their air of omnipotence, as if it were my fault they couldn't help me. *So, sue me if I don't want to take the latest drug that would help the arthritis but kill my liver. You try living without a liver.*

Despite my bias against medical doctors, I went down that rabbit hole. I messaged Greg, explaining that I was interested in learning about his story because I also had pain and was focusing on treating people with this condition. I wanted to believe he would be different, perhaps more understanding of what it felt like to be a patient who didn't know when he'd get better. Yes, he could understand all the complexities involved in surgery or what different diagnoses meant, but he was still being treated by a medical establishment that had yet to help him solve his pain. Just like me.

I considered that Greg was no longer in a position of authority to talk down to me as if I knew nothing. I might even be able to introduce him to a whole new world that might help him.

A few weeks later, once my predoc was done and I arrived in Portland, we met for a drink. Within the first few minutes he told me he had done his residency at Stanford in orthopedics. There are plenty of people who go to prestigious schools and never mention it unless it comes into conversation, and then there are people like Greg who feel the need to tell everyone about his titles and education because it gives him an identity and makes him feel important. I didn't care that he drove an Infiniti or lived in a condo he owned downtown or any of the other superfluous details about his status he made sure to mention. I immediately regretted my decision to meet with him.

I grew up in a nice neighborhood, I attended a small private Quaker school that prepped students for noteworthy colleges and universities, but I was taught to appreciate those things and not flaunt them. There was no need. Despite having low self-esteem in other areas, I never felt the need to shove my education or financial worth down someone's throat. I didn't really care what anyone chose to do with their money as long as they didn't try to impress me with what they had rather than who they were. Greg's display drove me crazy. The evening promised to be long.

Soon after our pleasantries were out of the way, he launched into the lengthy story of how he developed chronic pain. My ears perked up. After playing an aggressive game of tennis a number of years before, he'd found himself sore, which he chalked up to not having played for six months. The next day he played again but afterwards, it was "as though he would never be the same again." His dramatic wording made it clear that he'd told the story many times before and this one line had given him the most sympathy. He developed a pain in his groin, prompting him to spend the next months, then the next several years, trying to get a proper diagnosis. He ended up having two failed back surgeries. He exhausted medication and surgery in his quest to improve the pain. Eventually he found that he could no longer work.

That's where his story got really interesting. Greg had taken out two disability policies before the injury, which provided him the equivalent of his last salary. He lost nothing in wages, still held the doctor title, and gained a whole bunch of free time, stress-free. I definitely had my suspicions when Greg told me this as I had never heard of this type of policy before and wondered if he was working the system. I knew narcissists. They were smart and charming, and felt justified in any course of action that satisfied their needs, no matter who got hurt.

There's another diagnosis that's often comorbid (goes hand in hand) with narcissism: Antisocial Personality Disorder, which is not at all like what it sounds. It should really be renamed. Laypeople know those who suffer from the disorder as sociopaths or psychopaths even though the DSM-V never uses those words. As with narcissism, these people have an inflated sense of self-importance, but what's different is that they frequently manipulate or deceive others for their gain. They have a pattern of lying, avoid personal responsibility, and have no regard for how their actions affect others. Basically, they have no conscience and often feel justified in their actions as if they're somehow special. A key feature is their need to dominate others in order to get things like money, power, sex, possessions, as well as to feel in control. I know, sexy, right?

I felt Greg had a conscience and cared about others, but was that because another trait of both disorders is being outwardly superficial and charming? Moth to a flame, that's me.

Work for Greg had been very stressful. Before leaving his post at Stanford, he often threw up before performing a surgery, which suggested to me that he suffered from anxiety. He didn't like being criticized and, as a resident, criticism—or feedback—was precisely what one got. Developing a pain that doctors couldn't diagnose, or cure, seemed like an awfully good excuse for him to stop performing. Pull out of the game, and he wouldn't be told all the ways he wasn't good enough. He would no longer notice that he wasn't getting the praise his ego desperately desired.

Greg claimed that therapy had helped immensely in terms of learning to cope with his new life as someone with chronic pain. After his first back surgery, he couldn't bend over. When he accidentally dropped his wallet, he'd kick it to someone and ask him or her to pick it up for him, and it was done. He had to get special tools to put on his socks, so he was further invested. I learned all about Greg that night and the saga of why he was no longer a pain doctor.

After the first night meeting Greg, I wasn't inclined to go out with him again, but it appeared that we both had a lot of time on our hands, so I just fell into it, which is my MO. I was studying for an exam while also getting my postdoc up and running, which meant I spent an awful lot of time on my own. When Greg invited me to coffee so that I could study and he could read the news with company, I went because it was better than being by myself.

Over the course of the next few months, Greg and I hung out a lot. I enjoyed the intellectual stimulation, the riveting conversations—something I hadn't had since graduating. He also introduced me to his neighbor, who then introduced me to his friends, and I found myself enjoying the social aspect of our friendship, which naturally developed. I had a pal, someone to do things with in the city, who included me in social activities.

I waited awhile before I raised the possible connection between his pain and psychological issues. He refused to go there, even knowing this was my professional focus, because he was exempt from such nonsense. He reasoned that his pain was due to a physical cause, even though after years no one had been able to determine what, precisely, that was.

He's easily the smartest friend I had but if he refused to consider that there were other causes for his pain, then no amount of information from me or anyone else would get him to change his mind.

Greg is not an anomaly when it comes to a refusal to consider the psychological reasons underlying physical pain. I've been reticent to unearth my own issues at times. It feels never-ending, as if once you start peeling the layers of the proverbial onion there will be no end. That can feel overwhelming. Or, if you don't want to face the things you don't want to accept about yourself, then never uncovering those feelings safeguards you from doing so. Pointing to a physical cause, even if that cause is unknown is a lot easier to digest than accepting the traits about yourself you don't want to recognize. You're insecure, vulnerable, have low self-esteem, have a fake picture of yourself, on and on it goes. Learning those things about yourself is not easy for a lot of people to process; it is so much easier to focus on a physical cause and cure.

When my friends met him, they asked what I saw in him. Didn't I get tired of listening to the same old story of how he became injured, his inability to work, why he walks with a limp? I told them that we talked about other things. But they were right, whether we discussed politics, the state of Oregon, or the weather, the conversation inevitably came back to him and stayed there, while I listened.

I eventually found myself annoyed and drained. I realized the friendship wasn't working out, that I wasn't feeling gratified by hanging out with him. The lopsided conversations were something I could no longer tolerate. So, I decided to end it. I told him half of my reasoning because you can't tell a narcissist the full whammy of how self-involved they are. That kind of criticism makes them angry and they will only get defensive and make you wrong, which is exactly what he did. He told me that as a psychologist resident, the way I communicated my feelings was pretty lousy (which was probably true seeing how my repressed feelings go to pain, similar to most of my clients, because we don't know how to express what we need or want—but that wasn't the issue at hand).

A year and a half later, after I moved back to the Bay Area, Greg called me out of the blue and said he was in San Francisco. He asked to meet for a drink. *Why not? What could a quick drink hurt?*

When we met, I found him to be really different—more empathetic, softer somehow, warmer. He'd been engaged, he told me, bought the ring and everything, but because he and the girl kept fighting, they decided to end it. I wondered if heartbreak had changed him.

By the way, narcissism is a stable disorder, meaning it doesn't change, and people don't improve unless they're committed to getting better by working on their issues. Most narcissists never enter therapy because, as far as they're concerned, nothing is wrong with them. If they end up there it's likely because a partner or friend gave them an ultimatum or they sought therapy for other issues not related to their narcissistic behaviors. Nothing is ever their fault. Everyone else is at fault. There is hope for them, but they must be really committed to working on their issues and not deciding that everyone else is to blame. A supervisor in grad school once warned me and my classmates to only take on one patient with narcissistic personality disorder at a time in our caseload, because they are so immensely draining. I fooled myself into believing that Greg had changed. I was pretty sure he was a narcissist. Did he have the full-blown disorder? I wasn't his psychologist so I couldn't make that call for sure. But that's why I couldn't tolerate being friends with him the first time around and yet, I enjoyed spending time with him and having a male friend again so much that I really wanted to believe he had changed. Total delusion.

As a professional, I understood the deal, but nonetheless, Greg and I became closer than we had the first time around. Go figure.

Granted, I was invested in the idea of helping him, of getting him to consider alternative treatments. He found it interesting but still wouldn't go there in terms of departing from traditional medicine. I wanted him to have relief. I didn't want him to go against traditional medicine but rather, to see its limitations.

Six months into our new friendship, Greg was arrested. He told me his side of the story and I believed him. The details of the case aren't important. What is important was my desire to be there for someone who offered me very little in return.

He said that his few friends in Portland had abandoned him after the arrest. I figured his friends or acquaintances didn't care to know the full story; people who heard the story on the news had already decided the verdict on their own.

If everyone else had abandoned him, how would he not be grateful to me for believing in his innocence? The power dynamic was even more perfect.

As it happens, things weren't working out for me in San Francisco, so I decided that I would move back to Portland for a year to emotionally support him, to stand by him in his time of need.

I didn't have an ulterior motive, unless you consider it wanting a close friendship, wanting to be valued. I loved having a guy friend with whom I had an unspoken understanding that neither one of us fancied the other; we were strictly friends. I could talk to him about dating and relationship issues without him getting the slightest bit jealous, which is unusual, I think, for a single man and a woman. I'd even set him up with a friend of a friend. With Greg, I could talk about anything without being judged, and that last point is the golden nugget. He was in absolutely no position to judge me, and we both knew it. I would move heaven and earth to be around that. Most of the time, I sense that others will end up not just judging me, but also using me, and I'm always cautious as a result. Of course, this happened with Greg, again.

While I was emotionally supporting Greg, I had a

conversation with a guy I met online. I explained what had brought me back to Portland. The guy kept telling me that what I had done and was continuing to do for Greg seemed extreme, like something a wife or girlfriend would do, as opposed to a friend. He suggested that I had given up quite a lot of my own life to stand by this friend who didn't seem to offer much in return. It hit a nerve because his statements made me question what I was getting out of my situation with Greg. In a matter of a few months, I realized Greg hadn't changed at all.

I had signed up with a business coach as soon as I moved back to Portland. My coach helped me build my practice from scratch and every time he saw me at a seminar he asked about Greg. He noticed I invested a lot of time into my practice, but would take two steps forward and a giant step back. He attributed the backward momentum to my being around Greg and his negativity. My coach would tell me that I could only offer so much of myself before I had to let Greg go.

It's not that I suffered any physical symptoms at that time, but I wasn't happy. I still had tension that necessitated seeing chiropractors and massage therapists but nothing different than what I was used to. But I often felt anxious and depressed. Greg's issues took over way more mental energy than seemed normal. I would discuss his case with my friends and parents. My parents even met Greg during his ordeal. They felt bad for him. My mom really liked Greg. But they also cautioned me that I could only do so much. It wasn't my responsibility to change his mood. They likely noticed what was happening, I was so engulfed in Greg's issues that I was losing myself.

Once again, I said goodbye to Greg, with essentially the same reaction from him.

About a month later, after a period of no contact, he sent me a video of him training his dog that I had helped him pick out from a shelter. I watched it a few times. First, I watched it with the sound on. Then I turned the sound off and only watched Greg. He walked with ease, no limp. He squatted with no problem. It didn't seem like he was calculating how he walked. I wrote him back and told him he looked good, as if the pain wasn't bad and he was walking with more limberness. No response. I think he wanted a different reaction, one that didn't involve noticing his flexibility of movement; rather, he wanted a light-hearted comment about the dog, something to open up communication again.

A few months after that, while driving, I saw him walking to his car with his dog. He didn't see me. As soon as he got close to the car and didn't see anyone around except for a lone car (me) down the street, he walked easily to his car; his limp wasn't noticeable at all. It brought to mind my first concern when I met him: that he worked the system to get out of the emotional pain of being criticized. It was better to point to physical pain as the reason he couldn't work than to feel anxious or depressed that he wasn't smart enough or good enough at being a doctor.

CLIENT CASE: BEN

BEN CAME TO ME BECAUSE he felt stuck in his life. He had been living at home and hadn't moved on after graduating from college the year before. He considered hiking the Pacific Crest Trail but didn't follow through with it. Instead, he vacillated between applying for jobs around the country in his field, the one he majored in during college, and staying comfortable interning at a local company while living with his parents.

During my initial assessment, I found the feeling of emotional instability, of his not being sure of his feelings. He explained that it was difficult for him to relate to people. He didn't always know how to label his emotions, making it challenging to communicate and connect with his friends. When we traced this back to an earlier time, his body responded to age nineteen. At that time, he said that it felt as though his friends in college used him for his money or what he had, such as marijuana. He felt lonely because he felt like his friends weren't really his friends and were only interested in taking advantage of him.

When we explored his career, I tested for various emotions and found the feeling of false pride. False pride describes being less confident than one's bravado would indicate. Ben worried that he didn't learn as much as he should have in college. He even failed a few classes and took five years to graduate. He worried that he'd have to look things up once in a job and would feel dumb for not knowing what he thought he should know. Most of all, he feared he would let others down.

When I assessed for an original event—when false pride related to pursuing something important to him, combined with the fear of failure—his body responded to age twenty. There was a girl he met the summer before his junior year of college. She was the first girl he had really fallen for.

When he returned to school, they began Skyping every day for a few months. One day, out of the blue, she told him, "You know we're not dating, right? We don't need to talk so much." After that, she started distancing herself from him, not texting or Skyping the way she had. He put himself out there and she rejected him. Naturally, he felt like a failure.

False pride lives in the shame-based emotions, which include false self-assuredness, disgrace, wounded pride, dishonor, and self-consciousness. They cause a person to feel bad; to feel not good enough. Everyone feels these things from time to time, but the hope is that people won't become overwhelmed or get stuck there. Ben got stuck.

Ben allowed his feelings to blossom with The Girl but they weren't reciprocated and that rejection might as well have been a sword cutting his heart in half given the damage it did to him emotionally and the time it would take for him to heal and move on. He had no one to talk to because, in his mind, his friends didn't value him; they only valued what he had. He stuffed his emotions. The Girl's rejection permeated every other aspect of his life so that he became frozen in time, unable to move forward. He even described feeling as though he was trudging through deep mud. He got distracted by other things. He hadn't been able to fully complete any goal or endeavor since then.

When we discussed how his life might have flowed differently after the rejection, he said that he felt his energy shift. Up to that point, he used to be adventurous and was willing to take risks. When he changed majors that year, the last big risk he was willing to take, he found it far more demanding than he expected. He recognized that he had been stuck since that time and wasn't sure why. It seemed obvious to me that The Girl's rejection shattered his trust in others and even in himself so that putting himself out there in other areas of his life would seem as though he was setting himself up to be rejected again.

When I asked if there was anything else I should know, anything he wanted to tell me, he said around that same time, at age twenty, he lost the ability to swallow dry food. If he ate cereal for example, the food wouldn't go down his throat. This was eye-opening. Ben suffered an emotional heartache, a flat-out rejection from someone he cared about and in whom he was emotionally invested, and he developed a physical symptom as a result. He couldn't communicate his feelings to his friends, who were simply using him; he couldn't process them with The Girl, so he choked them down the way he choked down his food.

Staying isolated, going into emotional hibernation, turning off his feelings, even hiking the Pacific Crest Trail and not seeing or connecting with others for days would be a means to steer clear of people. It felt safer than moving forward and risking the uncertainty of rejection.

Our first goal was to process the festering pain of The Girl. We needed to go into the past and excavate the emotions he wasn't able to deal with at the time.

I had him think of what she said to him, the exact words of rejection that still took up mental and emotional space in his mind and in his heart. As hurtful as she was toward him, he still pined for her years later. Assessing his body for stored emotions, I found humiliation. He explained that he still had feelings for her even though she didn't return them, which was problematic because she remained in his hometown. I then identified frustration. Even though it would seem obvious why he had been frustrated with the situation, in order to bring the emotions to the surface where he could really feel them, I asked him to explain the cause of his frustration. He said that he couldn't understand why he couldn't move on and why he still cared about her and was drawn to her.

His homework for the next session was to journal to this prompt: "What am I willing to accept from her if I can't have what I want from her, which is a romantic relationship?" My goal was to help Ben get to a place of neutrality. I jotted down some other statements to test the following week such as "I'm OK with her. I'm OK without her. I'm OK with a relationship with her. I'm OK without a relationship with her."

At the next session, I was pleased that Ben had done his homework. His follow-through told me he was invested in working through his issues. He told me that he was willing to accept being good friends with The Girl. I told him to think of her and consider the fact that she'd never given him the relationship he desired and that she kept him at a distance. Keeping him at arm's length, I informed him, was essentially her way of saying "No," and yet he continued to pursue her. I then tested to find the emotion that was hiding underneath: irrationality.

"What doesn't make sense about this?" I asked Ben.

He thought about it and replied that he felt needy, like a chump, like he couldn't go with life's flow. He was hung up on one person and didn't know why. When I tested for an earlier event that echoed those same sentiments it went right back to three years before when she'd told him, "We're not dating."

Even though Ben felt The Girl was keeping him at a distance, they snapchatted every day. When I inquired about what they discussed, he explained that she was living overseas and would describe her new life and the guys she was interested in. From the sound of it, she was stringing along a few other guys like Ben.

Ben's homework after that session was to experiment with not responding to The Girl's snapchats. Apparently, she was used to telling him about her day and getting a response that would allow her to focus on herself. I wanted to see what came up for Ben when he didn't give her what she wanted. Did he feel doubt, anxiety, guilt? I told him it would also give him information about her response and suggested she would do one of three things: come forward and develop interest, be concerned, or be indifferent.

After a week of not responding to her prompts, Ben realized she was all about herself, as I had suspected. He understood that he would feel like even more of a chump even if she did want to date because the relationship would be solely about fulfilling her needs.

In order to make sure any residue was fully out of his system, I had him imagine The Girl dating someone else. When assessing the physiology of emotions, insecurity showed up. Ben wondered what other guys possessed that he didn't. Why would she choose someone else over him?

His homework for the next session: when she writes, only

respond with what's been going on in his life. The goal was to show him that, as self-centered as she was, she wouldn't make a good girlfriend even if she decided she wanted to date.

Ben began to see The Girl and the situation for what it was and realized he needed and wanted to move on from her. How to unhook himself, he wasn't sure. He needed some sort of closure.

I told him my challenge for the next week was to ask her what kind of response she wanted him to give her. Using that tactic would confront her to be honest about what she was doing. Her response would no doubt allow him to see just how little she cared about him.

The following week Ben said he felt really good about moving on and making decisions in his life for himself. I inquired about what had happened when he challenged The Girl. He realized she was so insecure that she needed a cadre of men around her in order to feel pretty. And with that, we started working on his career issues, which resolved within four more sessions. The Girl had kept him stuck; once he moved on from her, everything else fell into place.

HEROIN GUY

MY CLOSE FRIEND IN SEATTLE and I went out for some drinks one November evening. We had eaten very little before having one too many. While Jodee was talking to a guy next to her, someone wedged his chair in between me and the couple on the other side. It didn't seem to matter to him that there was no room for such a move. He said a few words to me. I was more forward and outgoing than usual, thanks to having a few drinks under my belt. I noticed that he was fat; not just ten to fifteen pounds overweight; he was carrying around an extra fifty.

I leaned over to Jodee and said, "We need to skedaddle ASAP. I have a Stage Five Clinger to my left who won't stop talking to me." Although I had liquid courage coursing through my veins, I had already found myself annoyed with the guy's constant questions and non-stop chatter. He was like a kid who keeps pestering adults with all his random facts in order to get attention. He asked what I did, when I told him I worked with athletes, among other populations, he told me he knew a lot of people in the city and might be able to help me make some connections. According to him, his aunt worked in the human resources department at the Mariner's for the past twenty years. She could easily put in a phone call to the manager and get me a meeting.

Nice enough, I thought, but I wasn't holding my breath. I tried talking to Jodee again but she was engrossed in conversation with some guy who seemed to be hitting on her.

The next day, much to my surprise, I received an email from the clinger, known from here on in as Heroin Guy, you'll understand why in a moment. I didn't remember giving him my card, which made me question how much I'd had to drink. His email was very polite. He reminded me that he was well connected in the city and could introduce me to the right people.

What would be the harm in meeting him to learn about his contacts, I figured. In other words, I wasn't interested in him as a boyfriend at all, but as a possible friend and business associate.

I was about to head to Victoria and Vancouver for Thanksgiving. We decided to meet the day before I left. Since all the coffee shops were closed by the time I was done seeing clients, I agreed to meet him at a bar down the street from my office. In the interim, he texted me a number of times. He told me that he had a ten-year addiction to opioids and was two years clean. Being clean and sober and doing it on his own was his greatest achievement. I tried to be supportive and yet, in the back of my mind, I wondered why he was disclosing this to me and what kind of opioids he'd used. Sometimes people disclose their skeletons in their closet soon after learning I'm a healer and I assumed that was what was going on.

From the get-go, Heroin Guy presented himself as a

broken human. Not only did he disclose his long history with drugs via text, he spent that first get-together discussing his ex-girlfriend, claiming she'd been abusive to him. I felt bad for him, sure, but I had no intention of anything beyond networking and forming a possible friendship. He seemed to have decided I was trustworthy enough to share his shoddy past, which is the quickest way to stroke my ego, to get my buy-in. I started to feel helpful by listening to him and that was the hook. That's what entangled me in the first place. He told me he admired my profession, which, no surprise, made me feel really good. He claimed that he needed to take some time to introduce me to the right people because he had to consider who he knew and how to go about it the right way. This seemed plausible to me. When we hugged goodbye, which felt a little awkward, I sensed it hadn't been a networking meeting for him at all, but a date.

My fears were realized the next day when Glinda, my dog, and I arrived in Victoria. He began texting me *all the time*. He said things that were way off base for a business colleague. I figured I could keep him at arms-length, nonetheless. I replied to him because I found him somewhat entertaining and, in retrospect, I didn't have a lot of friends to talk to every day. Beggars can't be choosers, as far as I was concerned.

After my hackles settled down, I considered my options. After months of dating men who were more interested in playing games, being non-committal, and only showing interest on the first date, I decided I was done with dating, at least online. I needed a break, pure and simple. Ghosting, hooking up without honesty, with vague intentions, showing a lot of interest during the chase, then feigning it once the guy got what he wanted, all took a toll on my self-esteem. The only solution I could find was to take a break from the scene, to stop pursuing what I really wanted and come up with a low-stakes alternative that didn't cost me anything emotionally.

Again, I wasn't the least bit attracted to Heroin Guy, but given my options—or lack thereof—I decided I could date him just long enough to get through the holidays, which, if you're single, can be a killer time of year. He was chatty and even if I found him annoying and wasn't attracted to him, I was tired of showing up stag at parties. The idea of bringing some guy to all the festivities, even if he was a loser, was more appealing than being around couples and feeling like the token single girl, again. He obviously liked to drink. At that time, it wasn't apparent how much of an issue it was for him. But it seemed innocuous enough to go out with him a few times as I headed into the next month or two of festivities.

I began to find his interest in me flattering. Unlike the jerks I had been meeting online, here was someone who made his interests known. I didn't have to guess that he was interested in dating me. He told me. And he texted me all the time.

When I told him that it was nice of him to tell me he was thinking of me, he lapped that up and told me twenty times a day, "I'm thinking of you." I wanted attention, who doesn't? But that level of constant attention began to feel smothering, like I was being engulfed.

In psychology, engulfment and abandonment often go hand in hand. One partner is afraid to be abandoned, in this case, Heroin Guy, so they over-immerse themselves into someone else's life in order not to feel alone. I already knew I was avoidant in relationships, that I was slow to warm up and really trust someone and feel close to him, and I had no intention of getting close to Heroin Guy. Engulfment was the last thing I wanted.

I'd seen this setup before.

Growing up, Dad was focused on business, so Mom wasn't getting her needs met. Instead of modeling good behavior, teaching me how to meet my own needs, she placed her needs on me so that I felt responsible for managing the inattentiveness from Dad. Add to that equation an emotionally distant father, and you've got someone like me. I've always been avoidant of people getting too close because I don't want to experience the same familiar feeling of being smothered, of having to take care of someone else's emotional demands.

I finally had to tell Heroin Guy to stop, that I didn't find his attention genuine. It was irritating to get so many of the same texts. He stopped. Then he told me how much he agreed with me, that hearing him tell me how often he was thinking of me would have been annoying. He became obsequious because all he wanted to do was please me and have me see him as good. He agreed with me on anything and everything. That became vexatious.

While still in Canada, I suggested a FaceTime call. We had been mostly texting, with a few sporadic phone calls. He was in the Virgin Islands with his family. He'd been getting drunk every night, but I didn't think too much of it as he was on vacation. When he showed up for our video call, he was completely wasted. He had glassy eyes and was pounding back another cocktail. I was pissed. I couldn't believe he didn't respect me enough to remain sober so we could have a decent conversation. It was another huge red flag that I didn't heed. He was so inebriated that he was slurring his words and repeating himself. "You are a doctor. You are not *my* doctor." Then he proceeded to repeat this about nine or ten times throughout the call.

When we hung up, I thought, *This is ridiculous. Why*

would I even consider going out with this guy when he has only been bothersome? Here was a man who had dropped out of college halfway through, got hooked on opioids for ten years, was four months out of a two-year relationship, and clearly not over his ex. He had a brother who died of a heroin over-dose four years prior and felt ashamed for giving the eulogy condemning heroin, because he used a pill form of it.

My parents would have had a field day had they known any of this, which, come to think of it, was probably part of the allure.

He kept texting and calling; he made it seem like his drunken state while on vacation wasn't the norm.

I had no reason to go out with him again, but I did. I doubted myself. I decided I should give the guy a chance because I was probably too picky for my own good; this was probably why I was still single. I didn't want to come off as mean and tell him I had no interest in him. That would have sounded duplicitous after texting and talking to him for two whole weeks, which would have made me no better than those who played me in the online dating world. That would have been the right thing to do, tell him I wasn't interested. That would have been showing boundaries; but to me, it felt hurtful, and I didn't know how to say "No" and trust myself.

Historically, I didn't go for strong men, people like Dad who may be wildly successful but completely self-absorbed. Sure, a strong guy might have real problems that could be helped with my support, but given my history with Graham and Dad, I knew those sorts of guys never admitted their weaknesses or flaws. I didn't want to get involved with a pow-erful man because I had my fill. From what I'd seen, those men are cold, detached, even mean, and definitely not appreciative of any well-meaning efforts on my part. Those types of men like to mentally masturbate and speak at you while thinking of themselves as the prize. I've never been interested in that type. The wounded bird was more to my liking; as long as I could focus on him and help him in some way solve his problems, it allowed me to be useful. I'm a healer after all and they're the ones in need of help. Everyone's a winner.

Truthfully, it was easier to date men I wasn't attracted to physically nor did I feel were my mental or emotional equals; I didn't have to invest much energy in them because I knew they were just temporary. Emotionally unavailable or immature men don't tend to want to discuss subjects in depth, which is good when you don't want them to discover how much is actually wrong with you. In a perfect world, I wanted the nerd who was interested in metaphysical subjects and ideas about the farther reaches of human consciousness and I also wanted to be attracted to him. But that kind of guy was dangerous. As soon as he asked me about my thoughts, as soon as he seemed to value my opinion, it would all be over. That would be too revealing. To feel good enough, I'd have to find fault with him so that I had an out, so that I wouldn't be seen for who I was, the girl who didn't have her life together, who wasn't pretty, thin, athletic, smart, and successful enough. By the same token, I remained emotionally unavailable as well, to safeguard myself from getting attached. Men won't put up with that obstacle for long before they tire and seek someone else.

On our first date for me, second for Heroin Guy, we went to dinner. He had already filled me in about his ex, Deanna, and continued to do so in every interaction we had. That night was no different. Over yet another drink, he tried convincing me that he was the victim and she was the narcissist/psychopath, using those terms as if he was parroting what his therapist told him without knowing what they meant.

Initially this drew me in. I had a history with narcissists; I'd grown up with them. That, combined with professional expertise, and I felt I could help him make sense of his relationship and move on. Yet I questioned myself for listening to Heroin Guy bemoan his ex, for not telling him early on that talking about her was inappropriate.

It would take another three months of constantly listening, offering recommendations, and hoping he'd move on from the ex for me to tell him over brunch, "Shut the fuck up! Seriously, what the fuck is wrong with you? Do you think I want to hear about Deanna? Your therapist is obviously not helping you. Just admit that she broke your heart and you're still in pain; instead of accepting that and working through the grief, you're adamant about making her wrong and yourself right and calling her names."

I shouldn't have let it get to that point.

I saw a deer in headlights looking back at me. I should have left right then and there, just like I should have never gotten involved with him in the first place. "You're right," he said. "I needed that. I needed that hard line. I mean everyone around me told me that Deanna was a narcissist, so I think I'm right about that, but I don't know why I kept talking to you about her. Because you kept asking and listening and I felt like you understood. But you're right. You're the last person I should have talked to about her."

When he sensed that I was contemplating moving on, he brought up the connections he'd dangled the first night we met. "My aunt said she can make the call to the Mariners' manager but you're not ready. Let's not waste this kind of connection until it's the right time."

I was floored. Where did he get off telling me I wasn't ready? So, I asked him why he didn't think I was ready. He told me I needed more experience meeting with coaches and working with baseball players. I told him I'd met with the Phillies the year before, but it didn't work out because I wasn't in the area full time. And whether I worked with baseball players or football players it was the same outcome: the athletes got better.

It didn't matter. Deep down I knew that this was his way of trying to keep me with him. I wanted the Mariners' connection, but I soon realized I didn't want it through Heroin Guy.

Only a few weeks into dating him, I lost my appetite, completely. Not eating contributed to being tired, something I loathed because it made me feel lazy and not productive or driven.

My body felt the problem, how mismatched we were. My body knew what my mind didn't want to admit. Thus, the lack of appetite. My body understood that I wouldn't be able to cope without eating and that I'd have to figure out the emotions getting in the way. If I figured out how Heroin Guy was so wrong for me by understanding my bodily symptoms, I'd dump him once and for all. My mind might find a way to put up with the problem, but my body just wouldn't tolerate my choices.

Sure enough, my loss of appetite concerned me enough to seek help. I didn't think it was anything serious and my intuition told me it was connected to repressed emotions. When I did some work with a colleague, using the same techniques I use with clients, she found that all my inequalities with Heroin Guy affected me and as a result, they caused my appetite to disappear.

She asked me to think of Heroin Guy while she tested my muscle. It was weak, indicating that something about him was not congruent or OK with me. She discovered that I was feeling lost or helpless to change the situation with Heroin Guy, that on an unconscious level I was stifled. I didn't want to admit to myself or to tell Heroin Guy that all his short-comings made me question why I ever went out with him. By identifying what I didn't admit to myself, I was able to bring those feelings to the surface. Once I admitted to myself that Heroin Guy was not well suited for me, my appetite improved.

But that didn't stop me from dating him. Neither did the pain in my back, neck, shoulders, or hands, not even a UTI. My body and mind were miserable with Heroin Guy, but I deluded myself and justified why I should try dating a mismatch.

If my boundaries had been stronger I would have told him, "I'd like to hang out with you as a friend but I don't feel a spark with you and in order to date, I need that spark." I felt like I led him on because I was never straightforward with my intentions. I thought maybe I should be open to dating someone who wasn't my type. Maybe I'd be pleasantly surprised. I was surprised, alright. Just not in a good way. I'd trapped myself.

While I was sorting out my various physical symptoms, Heroin Guy offered to take care of Glinda while I went up to British Columbia, Canada, for four days to attend a seminar on PSYCH-K, a healing technique to assess and dissolve dis-empowering beliefs. The fact that I was attending a training brought to my conscious mind that I really enjoy learning and self-growth, something Heroin Guy talked about, but never did anything about.

Glinda had been at his place before, but I thought I would sleep over with her so that she could get used to staying there. At some point in the night, I heard Glinda making a familiar sound. She was clearly about to throw up. *Nooooo.* My natural inclination was to reach Glinda in time so I could prevent her from ruining Heroin Guy's carpet. I leapt from the bed and on my way down the stairs my foot slid out from underneath me and I bounced down three or four stairs on my ass.

Ow, ow, ow, ow. Fuck, fuck, fuck. Fuck, fuck, fuck. I tried not to say it out loud, but my ass thumping down the stairs was anything but quiet.

Heroin Guy awoke. "Are you OK?"

"Yep, totally fine. Really. Just slid down a few stairs. Need to check on Glinda. Will be up in a few."

"Let me help you."

"No, really I'm fine. Please don't. Just go back to bed."

I didn't want him anywhere near me. There was nothing he could do. He wasn't a comfort for me. Being around him was fun as long as we had a few drinks and that was it.

It wasn't an accident that I slipped down his stairs. My body and mind were giving me another wake-up call that I refused to respond to. On top of all the other issues, now I'd hurt my tailbone. I didn't want to be at his place or dating him. I was constantly going against my intuition and judgement. I slipped down his stairs because I didn't see where I was going just like I didn't see or acknowledge the signs and symptoms my body was giving me. I specialize in looking at how physical symptoms are manifestations of unexpressed emotions. Even though I know it's harder to see issues within myself, I have still been able to recognize it. But I was being stubborn when it came to Heroin Guy.

As much as I have told myself I want a long-lasting relationship, I kept myself safe from having just that by dating men who weren't right for me in various ways. None of them seemed to have the full package. I dated lawyers and doctors to whom I wasn't attracted; I found the guy who did it for me physically, but left me feeling empty in every other way. When I was younger, in my twenties, my favorite type was the guy who lived too far away from me to make it possible to be with him—easier to fantasize about what could be than to fail at something and feel the rejection and sadness. Better to have never loved and therefore not lost than to go through the pain of loving and losing what's most precious.

I understand where this tendency comes from. I felt so unseen as a child that I concocted the idea of pretending to have pain in order to get my parents to pay attention to me. I wasn't enough, even though I was considered a star athlete. Even though I excelled at all of my after-school activities, such as ballet, horseback riding, gymnastics, and tennis, I still wasn't as good as my brother, no matter how hard I tried. I still feel as though I'll never be good enough.

How does this never good enough feeling translate into how I show up in relationships? I never feel that a guy will like me for me. I have to offer more or do more or show up in some big way that will make him really take notice. If I offered nothing but my presence and attention, the guy would see someone who sees herself as always being five to ten pounds heavier than she wants to be (and criticizes herself every day for it), feels lazy and unproductive and can never do enough of the right things to get ahead or be successful. They would see someone who doubts her decisions, is emotionally detached, and guarded; they would see someone who isn't fun, doesn't know how to mingle (the wallflower at parties), and who thinks more than she feels.

Emotional detachment is just not sexy.

I sat with Glinda for a few minutes and started to cry softly so Heroin Guy wouldn't hear me. I cried because I was in a lot of physical pain, but I also cried because I realized how messed up I'd allowed my situation to become. Was I with someone I knew wouldn't work out to keep myself safe from feeling and thereby avoiding the risk of getting hurt? Would I actually be able to feel deeply with someone I was attracted to on many levels? Possibly, but that would create its own problems. I know I would be scared to be with someone who truly sees and hears me. I wouldn't be able to hide and that might be too revealing. But my body would likely respond favorably, the way it did with Apartment Boy—that continues to be my incentive in finding someone who's right for me. Why couldn't I feel anything at all for Heroin Guy? Why was I with someone I wasn't even attracted to? Glinda and I sat like that for about five minutes and being with her comforted me more than anything.

Two weeks after breaking up with Heroin Guy for good, I went to my chiropractor. He asked what I'd been doing differently. "I finally broke up with a guy who was absolutely awful for me. Why do you ask?" He told me that my range of motion was greatly improved and the knots he had been working on for the past months had completely melted. Yep, that was my body speaking to me loud and clear. I ignored it and paid the price for the five months I was with Heroin Guy.

CLIENT CASE: HENRY

HENRY HAD BEEN SUFFERING FROM back pain for three months before he found me. He explained that he had surgery on his back twenty years ago. Things had improved but from time to time his back muscles would flare and he'd experience pain again. Things took a turn for the worse a few months prior to our meeting and he had no idea why. He hadn't fallen or sustained an injury of any kind. He reported that the pain just came on out of the blue.

At age fifty-eight, he didn't accept the usual paradigm that he was simply getting old and this was his new reality. The pain didn't make any sense, especially since it had come on so suddenly. He said that his inability to get out of a chair without straining was disheartening. Even small activities like lifting and carrying groceries for his wife were now impossible without being worn out.

Henry was embarrassed by how little he could do and how he thought he appeared to others, like an old man, unable to even get out of a car with ease. Although his wife never told him that he looked like a feeble, old man, that's how he felt. He felt bad for his wife, for what she had to put up with, and he just wanted to get back to having the kind of fun they were both used to.

When he considered why the pain was there, he went through a list of all the injuries he suffered throughout his lifetime. There was a softball injury in his thirties, as a teen he somehow threw out his back, twenty-five years ago, he strained his back while moving. As a music teacher he even wondered if his bad posture had finally caught up with him given all the instruments he taught others to play.

Initially, I assessed the back pain to see if there was an emotional connection and found there was one. It was connected to his friend, Brittany. As mentioned before, when a connection has to do with someone else in the client's life, it's normally about the client—because it's easier to look at and understand other people's behaviors and emotions rather than turning the spotlight on one's self. Brittany was the entry point that led us to her partner whose emotions resonated with Henry.

We can pick up on the emotional reaction of others, even if we're not fully conscious of it. For Henry, he was sensitive to Brittany not expressing her emotions. I asked him to piece together how that might be showing up for her. He explained that she was the partner of another friend who'd been very sick. Henry noticed that ever since his friend became ill, he had become very negative and pessimistic. He didn't like asking for help and would have preferred that no one knew he was ill. Henry wanted to be there for his friend but didn't know what to do.

I traced those feelings back to when Henry was twenty-eight years old. I asked him where he was and what he was doing at that age. He talked about being in grad school, the courses he was taking, his friends, his family. None of it was testing as being something that had any importance or relevance to what he was going in the present. I asked about relationships he was in or had been in and he mentioned two women. As he said their names, I tested his strength and he was weak on the second woman's name. I asked him to tell me about her and it turned out that she was someone he was seeing on the side of a more serious relationship. The side action lady was exciting and new. She was outgoing and had a lot of spark. The chemistry was intense, and he carried on with her knowing full well that she wouldn't be the woman he'd marry. He would marry his wife, who happened to be the one he was seeing seriously at the same time.

He was embarrassed recounting this information. He knew that being unfaithful to his steady girlfriend was wrong and he didn't want people to see him in that light and to think badly of him, so he hid the extracurricular relationship. Apparently, he did a good job because no one found out.

When I assessed his back pain further, I found that the pain going up and down his spine had its roots in his personal space. By looking at the various categories of money, love, and all the roles he plays, his body weakened on the concept of money. The money category includes all material things, even physical and emotional space. When I checked for what emotion was connected to his personal space, I found the feeling of desperation. I asked Henry to explain how he felt desperate about his personal space in the present. He described himself as being self-conscious by nature and didn't like taking up space or being seen as someone who seeks sympathy or attention. With the onset of his back pain, that's precisely what he found himself doing out of desperation for relief.

Looking for an earlier event where he might have felt similar, I landed on age thirty-five. Henry recounted a move he made with his wife to a new city and state. He found himself being forced to make cold calls in order to find work; as anyone who's had to make such calls knows, it forces you to put yourself in an uncomfortable place mentally and emotionally. Henry already had issues with bringing attention to himself and he had no choice but to do just that in his new job. In the present, bringing attention to himself because of pain and his inability to do things for himself, had brought him back to that uncomfortable era.

When I gave Henry my report of findings at our follow-up session, I started by asking him whether he felt any pain relief after the intake. I also opened it up for him to give me his feedback on how the session had been for him. He was angry—at me. He admonished me for not being more forthright about my psychic abilities. "Nowhere on your website do you say that you're psychic and can tell people things about themselves just by asking them a few questions."

I asked him to explain why he thought I was psychic and he told me my ability to discover the affair he'd had in his twenties was uncanny. He hadn't told anyone about that, not even his wife, and the fact that I found it within minutes made him uncomfortable. Henry wanted to know why I even brought it up, particularly since he'd all but forgotten the incident.

I told him that although it might look like I'm a psychic (man, would that solve a lot of my problems!) I assured him I'm not. I told him the reason I was able to pinpoint a certain time in his life had everything to do with what he was presently experiencing. He didn't like being in pain because it forced him into the spotlight. His experience of seeing two women at twenty-eight surfaced because it was something he had been hiding all this time. It still brought shame and embarrassment and I suggested that it was time to process the memories from that time. By doing so, he wouldn't have to hold onto old wounds, which would in turn free up the pain he felt in his back. The continued need to repress those memories were still hanging over him. By giving them the space to be looked at and observed, he would be able to release them.

LUNCH WITH MY PARENTS

I'D BEEN LIVING IN THE Russian Hill neighborhood of San Francisco during grad school for about a year when my parents decided to pay me a visit. They invited Drew to lunch, the friend who had driven cross country with me. Even before this occasion, Mom would constantly ask me, "Are you sure he's gay? He would make such a good companion for you."

"Yep, Mom, I'm sure he's gay."

Little did she know, Drew and I tried being more than friends four months after we connected. It had been a complete disaster.

At lunch, my dad initially monopolized the conversation. He seemed to enjoy spewing answers to all the questions thrown his way. Drew was really good at asking questions and getting a lively conversation going. It's one reason my mom adored him. She adored anyone who asked about her, her past and present as an actress, her life in general. My dad reveled in that as well and loved talking about his achievements and knowledge of the law.

I was aware that my dad would drift off if the conversation didn't include him or if we didn't discuss one of his numerous areas of expertise, which would allow him to pontificate. I wasn't sure how visible this tendency to dominate and grandstand was to others.

At one point, I asked my dad something, a follow-up question to better understand what he was discussing, and he didn't hesitate to squash me, making me sound like an idiot.

He had been discussing one of his high-profile cases. You would have thought I knew a lot about law from listening to my dad talk about it so much, but the opposite was true. I often zoned out, thought of other things while he went on and on about how much he knew about life in general and being a defense attorney. I suppose I just didn't enjoy listening to him puff himself out in such a way that demanded attention and yet felt so cold. It was as if he didn't take into consideration how any of his clients felt, how their lives must have been traumatized while going through a difficult trial. But then again, I came to realize that most lawyers don't get emotionally invested in their clients, much like how I had to keep some distance from my clients in order to serve them.

My ears perked up when my dad mentioned the name of one of his clients I had met while in high school, someone I really liked and admired. I knew of his case but wasn't sure of all the details and when I asked for clarification my dad made sure to make me feel as if I never paid attention and couldn't retain anything even if he had told me one hundred times.

"Did Wade's reputation ever get fully reinstated," I asked. "I mean after he got fired from that boarding school. Even though you helped him win the case I can imagine that something like that stays with you for a long time, like a shadow. It's not like he got an apology from that school. I mean other schools probably knew about the lawsuit and were less inclined to hire him."

"My dear," (something my dad often called me and my mom when he was explaining something he thought we should already know) "do you only listen to the things you want? What are you actually learning or remembering from your doctoral degree in psychology? I won the case with Wade and helped him get a huge settlement that changed his life. I showed you the letter he wrote me, didn't I? The one where he explicitly told me I made a huge impact in his life?"

I was embarrassed and I shut down. I hardly spoke for the rest of the lunch. My dad never noticed how he made me feel, never seemed to consider how his demeanor was so demoralizing that I stopped participating in the conversation, but it wouldn't have changed anything if I could get him to acknowledge it. He didn't want to feel wrong about his behavior. He likely would have defended it. I'd feel the same either way, whether I stood up for myself and called him on how he made me feel or whether I said nothing. My mom never called him on his behavior, whether he was putting her down or me.

He spoke that way to her as well, and she generally took it in stride. Not once would she correct him or let on that her feelings were hurt. Not at the moment at least, but it would come out later to me. She would vent and tell me all the things about my dad she didn't like or agree with, something I only learned was unhealthy from a therapist in grad school. The therapist I met with a few years later told me that when one parent talks badly about another parent to the child behind the other parent's back it's really detrimental for the child. It makes the child feel he or she has to pick a side and see one parent as all bad and the other parent as all good and truthful.

After I earned my doctoral degree, I tried to tell my mom that she should speak directly to my dad because he would remain unable to read her mind. But she never did. When I would bring up something she had complained to me about, such as her strong desire to sell the farm—the one she and my dad had taken over for my grandmother—my dad acted as though it was the first time he heard of her dissatisfaction. I then found myself in the role of mediator. Of course, my mom would act as though she had told my dad plenty of times that she hated the farm and wanted to sell it, but he didn't listen because he only listened when he wanted to. Essentially that was what my dad was accusing me of when he put me in my place at lunch. Maybe my family has an issue with tuning things out that don't interest us. My dad would act surprised, my mom would adamantly protest that she had brought her issues with the farm to his attention numerous times, and I wouldn't know who to believe; I ended up feeling crazy for being involved in the first place.

We all had our ways of reacting to Dad when he put us down. I shut down. My mom looked down, shook her head in disagreement, in silence—then vented to me later. And Graham, well, he yelled back and would be even more hostile than usual. Perhaps that's where his condescension developed, from his need to defend but then it turned into his way of communicating to the rest of the family.

The times I tried to call my dad on his behavior he threw up his hands and told me I was speaking psychobabble. If that didn't work to shut me up, he laughed it off and removed himself from the conversation. I never once heard him take responsibility for putting others down or acknowledge that he might be wrong.

My dad was never wrong. I wasn't the only one to notice. His need to be right was so pronounced that everyone who spoke at his funeral service (which took place ten years later), commented on this trait, along with his competitive nature. I recalled a heated argument he seemed to be enjoying, "Dad, do you want to relate, or do you want to be right?" He laughed and seemed pleasantly surprised at my exasperation.

"Well that's a stupid question; I want to be right."

That need to be right was more than evident at our lunch that day. Fortunately, chatty Drew always had something else to talk about, so he let my dad finish, then changed the subject.

After my parents split the restaurant scene, Drew gave me the empathy my dad had not. He tried to soothe things for me by expounding on the fact that a lot of high-powered attorneys and people who have held important positions are simply inept when it comes to emotional intelligence. It helped having a friend witness what I dealt with in my family, the dynamics that had always made me feel ashamed. My dad's condescension wasn't just in my imagination; it was obvious to others. I knew I had good reasons for stuffing my emotions.

LOSS AND HOW I
DEAL (OR DON'T
DEAL) WITH IT

My dad loved to argue. He did it in such a way that the more heated the discussion became the more I could tell he was enjoying it, which only frustrated me more. He had to be right, at all costs. I look back now and wonder if "losing" an argument meant that he had somehow failed. Needing to be right, plus being a defense attorney, equals winning. He would never put me down per se, but when we engaged in conversation I always worried that we'd go head-to-head on a sensitive topic, one that exposed me as somehow stupid, or worse, revealed my true feelings, something I wanted to avoid. That's the summary of my relationship with my father, a series of arguments that always left me defensive and angry.

Every year on my birthday, my mom would recount how cold it was the week she brought me home from the hospital that first time. She told me how the doctors had told her that she had cervical cancer—they'd discovered it while she was in labor—and how she was so grateful that we both ended up being OK. She teared up and started to cry. My Dad, not knowing how to empathize or show any compassion when people were vulnerable, ridiculed her. Laughing and mocking her, he asked, "Are you crying? Why are you crying?" Inevitably, that made her stop and repress her emotions, which made him feel more comfortable. I knew this about my dad, this tendency, and didn't want to be the target of his derision.

Many years later, I came across books on the topic of emotionally immature parents and childhood emotional neglect. No therapist had ever pointed to these concepts. Instead, they all suggested my parents and brother suffered from various personality disorders, which fit, but learning about these other concepts really helped me understand why I shut down when I was younger. You're supposed to feel comfortable being vulnerable with your family. That's the very first place you're meant to learn how to tolerate emotional distress and feel free to express yourself; it's where you should be able to communicate feelings that are scary and which are uncomfortable to reveal and to know that you'll not only be OK, you'll be loved.

That's not the experience I had.

Watching the way my dad mocked anyone in the family when they showed sadness and observing how my mom rarely demonstrated any outward show of grief taught me that it was better to rope in any feelings that had the possibility of making me feel ashamed and humiliated.

Of course, the same didn't apply to my dad. In the unlikely event that my dad caught the feeling bug and started to cry, everyone else had to be as gentle as possible with his fragile state. God forbid anyone showed him the same behavior he expressed to others when they were upset.

Sadness just wasn't acceptable in my family, and if I showed any sign of ignorance, my dad was certain to shove my nose in it and remind me how much I didn't know, making me feel embarrassed by my lack of knowledge. He, in turn, would feel that much more intelligent and confident. It's like he derived energy from bullying me into admitting I didn't know something. This, I've come to learn, is a trait of narcissistic personality disorder. Not that I need to label his issue or clinically diagnose him, but let's face it, I'm trained in clinical psychology, and that's what I've learned to do. The narcissist will puff himself out to look more capable and confident of himself, all to minimize his lack of self-worth. The narcissist, as I understand it, lacks empathy, believes the world revolves around him, has grandiose ideas of himself, sees himself as more famous, popular, or liked than he actually is, and comes off as entitled.

The clinical diagnosis involves these criteria and includes being preoccupied with fantasies of success, power, or beauty; believes that he or she is unique or special and therefore can only be understood or associate with other special people; takes advantage of others to get their own needs met; is often envious of others or feels others are envious of them; and shows arrogant behavior. A clinical diagnosis requires that five out of nine criteria are met. I'm pretty sure Dad would have scored top of the class if he'd taken that diagnostic test. And he probably would have been proud of that accomplishment, too.

My dad was the king of bubble bursting. If I felt good about something, he was going to make sure I left the conversation deflated, as if that were his job. When I approached a former Seattle Seahawk and asked if he would be open to working with me I was ecstatic when I got a quick response that was super positive. My mom was supportive and encouraging. "Honey, that's fantastic!"

Dad had more questions. "Where'd he go to college?"

"I don't know," I replied.

"You don't know? You need to know this."

"Why?" I asked. "He's not in college anymore so why does it matter?"

"Because it does. It matters where he went and who coached him." He sounded more like a parent dealing with a small child—As long as you live under my roof, I make the rules and you follow them.

More questions came, ones I didn't see as pertinent to treating the player for issues he'd developed since being on the team.

"What was his position?" My dad decided this was the question that was most important. I needed to know way more about this guy than I thought; that was the lesson he meant to instill.

I looked up the former Seahawk, told my dad where he went to school and then said, "He was a long snapper." I had no clue what a long snapper did (it sounded more like a fish to me). So, I asked my dad to explain the position to me. I could have been a smartass about it, but something told me he was trying in his own way to be genuine and help me know more about my subject. At least, that's what I hoped. Sure, I could label him a narcissist, but he did have his positives. He did want to help, even though he went about it entirely the wrong way. "Do you know what a long snapper does?" I asked him.

Much to my chagrin my dad said, "I actually have no clue." He shook his head as if it was strange that he didn't know this position. "Look it up," he told me.

I looked up the position on Google and described it to my dad. Listening, my dad enacted what a long snapper does, which was quite helpful and saved me from looking it up on YouTube. He was being a hardass and although he almost sucked the air out of my happy balloon, I knew this was his way of relating, that he didn't know any other way, and so I let him off the hook. My natural impulse would be to take aim, get a pot shot in when I had the chance, point out his lack of expertise, but I decided to let him win.

At one point, however, Dad and I got into a heated argument. The topic eludes me now but I remember being so upset with him and his constant need to be right, his need to put me down, so he could feel better about himself, that I remember thinking, *I won't miss you when you're gone.*

So much for bad karma.

After less than two years of living in Philadelphia, I drove cross-country from Philly to Portland with a colleague from work. Earlier that year, a friend I had met in Portland got married. She made me her maid of honor and every time I visited Portland to help with the wedding, my heart tugged at me to move back. I felt like I always wanted to be in Portland but either my education and career pulled me away or I caved to Mom's pressure. I decided to keep my practice in Philly while I made my way back to Portland. Eventually, I would choose one or the other. I was heavily leaning toward Portland.

Mom was livid. But she could tell she wasn't getting through to me, so my dad took up the cause and got on my case about living in Portland for a fourth time. At the dinner table one evening on a brief visit to Philly in October, a month after I had left, my dad laid into me.

"Serena, you've lived all over the world—Paris, London, Sydney, New York City, and San Francisco—why are you going back to Portland? Don't you remember when you were living in London and you would tell people where you had just moved from and no one had any clue where Portland,

Oregon was? If you want to live on the West Coast, pick a bigger city with more going on. Go back to San Francisco, or move to San Diego, or Los Angeles, or even Seattle. Why Portland, Oregon, again? You're pursuing sports and working with athletes. All those other cities have more opportunities than Portland."

It got me thinking; rather, it got me doubting myself and my decisions just like I did with any choice with which my parents didn't agree. It didn't matter to them that I had always loved Portland. That perhaps all my moving was in an effort to find another city where I felt at home like I did from the moment I visited Portland before college. After my Philly visit, I took a few trips to Seattle and decided I would move up there to test the waters, even though I knew no one.

A week after moving to Seattle at the end of January, I was online, searching for a dresser. My mom called. Even before she opened her mouth, my intuition sounded the alarm. She wasn't going to deliver good news.

Let me back up.

In December, my dad had undergone an operation to replace four valves in his heart. He only ended up needing to get two replaced but it was still a major operation. He came through it like a champ but then developed pneumonia, which he also beat.

Talking to him six weeks post-surgery, it sounded like my dad was in good spirits, albeit frustrated that he hadn't played tennis or done anything athletic for that length of time. An athlete, he was generally tough and in good health. Three years prior, at age seventy-three, he climbed Mt. Kilimanjaro with very little training. He roughed it on week-long kayaking trips that took him across the globe, skied double black diamonds, played tennis a few nights a week, rode horseback, and biked on the weekends. He was in tip-top shape. I thought he'd come through his recovery with flying colors and be good as new in a relatively short period of time. But two weeks later, his lowered immunity was too weak for the sepsis he contracted when going to the hospital for a checkup.

It didn't make sense that he would die, especially not after battling the pneumonia without realizing anything was wrong.

I heard my mother say the words over the phone. Glinda, with her higher senses, knew something was up. She got up, looked at me with concerned eyes, and then my mom told me, "Dad died." Her voice was shaky, but she didn't cry. "I wanted to tell you first, before Graham." My mom has often told me she thinks I'm mentally stronger than my brother. Perhaps she thought I'd handle the news better.

"OK," I said. I kept repeating it like it was the only word I knew. "OK. OK. OK."

My heart sank.

Mom explained how he had been in and out of the hospital over the past few days as she had told me via email the week before. She figured this last visit was no different; she assumed he just needed another check-up and he'd be fine. I could hear how shocked she was and close to crying, but she never let her feelings take over. Mom described how she went home after dropping Dad off; how her hair was still wet from the shower when she got the call that she needed to be back at the hospital as soon as possible. By the time she got there, the doctors were unsuccessfully trying to resuscitate him and she had to make the decision to pull the plug or let him live like a vegetable.

She chose the former and because she kept telling me this story, I knew she was questioning whether she made the right decision. It was during those times, when she recounted making the decision, saying good-bye to her partner of forty-five years, that she got close to crying but she held it in. She was telling me the details rather than exhibiting any feeling around the gravity of the situation. It likely wouldn't have made much difference if she had emoted. These are my people. We report; we don't emote.

I heard it all, but it went in one ear and out another. I went blank, numb. Dad was dead. He hadn't been tough enough. When we talked the night before his surgery, back in December, I worried that he might not make it but chalked that up to my anxiety and worst-case-scenario tendencies. Perhaps my intuition was stronger than I knew. Now, here we were.

"OK, thank you for telling me." I honestly can't remember what, exactly, I said before I hung up. It certainly wasn't, "How are you doing?" Or, "I love you." Or even, "I'll call you soon." Neither of us had the capacity to comfort one another. We didn't know how.

I didn't know what to do. After I hung up, I went back to searching for dressers online.

Twenty minutes later it hit me, and I cried. I cried for the next seven days.

At one point, I thought I saw Dad walking down the street. Had it been a cruel joke? As I got closer, I realized it was someone who dressed similarly and had his looks. I thought it wasn't true. I had all sorts of irrational thoughts and beliefs. The author Joan Didion calls this magical thinking.

I did miss him when he went. You can't prepare for death. It happens. No matter whether you had a contentious relationship or not, it always feels like there wasn't enough time.

I reached out to a few friends, but I didn't actually want to talk to anyone. I had no idea how to put any of this grief into words. And what could anyone say to help me make sense of the situation? Growing up, Mom and Dad had inadvertently taught me that no one else could make me feel better with words alone; that I would have to solve things on my own. What would talking to a friend do, especially when I wasn't even in touch with my feelings?

I cried here and there, but only in private. Sometimes I felt the tears coming on while taking the elevator in my apartment building and immediately tried to pull it together, in case someone else got on.

Meanwhile, life continued. I went on a few dates. On one date, the guy talked about losing his father and the stress of closing his estate. It sounded like it had happened recently, but he lost him fourteen years earlier. It would have been an excellent opportunity to tell him about my loss, but I held back. I worried that I would break down and cry in front of him, a complete stranger. Crying in front of a close friend made me embarrassed; the thought of crying in front of someone who may have understood my behavior, yet who's reaction I couldn't gauge, made me resistant to doing that. I also feared criticism. I imagined he would look at me and tell me I wasn't ready to be dating, that I was probably still in shock and needed more time to grieve, essentially rejecting me right there on the spot. Turns out it wouldn't have mattered if any of those scenarios played out because he never followed up after that one date anyway.

A month after I got the news about my dad, I took a trip to Chicago to attend a two-day workshop on practice management that I had planned before my dad passed. It was given at a hotel and despite being February, the air conditioning was cranked so high I wore my puffy coat to stay warm. It didn't work. I got sick. And I couldn't kick it.

I developed a respiratory cough and started getting tired. I went to the community acupuncture clinic down the street when I returned to Seattle.

As soon as the acupuncturist told me that lungs are connected to grief in Chinese medicine I started to cry. And I kicked myself for not knowing better. I studied this connection for some of the interventions I use with clients. I knew lungs and grief were connected but didn't notice the signs when they affected me. When I told the acupuncturist about my dad, I could see tears well up in her eyes, which only made me sadder. I'm no different than others—sometimes the pain I'm going through doesn't register until I see how someone else reacts. Suddenly, I can't pretend it's not there.

Just like my experience after 9/11, I tried dealing with the trauma on my own. I did a lot of self-reflection but never had anyone listen to the array of feelings that often accompany a loved one's passing. I had friends who offered an ear, and at one point I asked for a select few to check in more, but somehow it wasn't enough. I got tired. Even unloading the dishwasher exhausted me to the point that I would take an hour nap afterwards.

Much like the circumstances in my life post 9/11, I had a few acquaintances in Seattle, but no close friends. A friend in Portland offered to come visit—insisted on it, in fact—but I felt bad that she would have to make the three-hour trip so assured her I was fine. I was in a new city and bottled everything up.

This, after going through a doctoral degree in psychology, studying advanced mind body interventions that access the physiology of emotion to pinpoint the feelings that have been repressed, and working with many people and helping them heal their physical and emotional ailments by helping them find and release their unexpressed emotions.

I was a pro at repression and when something happened as traumatic as my dad dying unexpectedly, I did not have the protocols in place to adequately deal with it. That was the petri dish for developing a somatic issue. For me, it came in the form of fatigue. My body and mind know I've built up a tolerance to all sorts of pain, but fatigue makes it difficult to move forward in life and achieve my goals. It's the one thing that forces me to seek out answers because fatigue makes it impossible to have a normal life.

When death happens again, which it will because it's inevitable, I will reach out to more friends. I will request their presence and tell them that my habitual ways of coping don't help (which they already know), and ask them to be present, because presence alone is very healing. Being seen and heard and allowed to have whatever feelings arise without having to change them or hide them will ideally let me feel my emotions without letting them get stuck in my body.

CLIENT CASE: REGINA

LIKE SO MANY OF MY clients, by the time Regina found me, she had already seen countless doctors who hadn't been able to solve her issues. Some were medical specialists who ruled out certain conditions and took X-rays and MRIs, which showed no abnormalities. Some were holistic practitioners ranging from chiropractors and acupuncturists to iridologists and reiki practitioners. It had been three years and she wanted answers. She was open to trying my services after reading good reviews online.

Regina was forty years old and suffered from back pain that went into her abdomen and developed gradually over a year. All other healers, according to Regina, hadn't helped. If she felt any better, the relief only lasted for forty-eight hours. Even strong pain medications failed to ease her pain.

Before we got into the exam of looking for repressed emotions, she disclosed that she had wanted children for many years and finally became pregnant only to lose the baby three months later. A year later, the pain developed.

174

Using muscle testing, I assessed for whether her back pain was connected to her emotions and found a link. Next, I found that the emotional connection had to do with the category of love. Again, love can be about anyone the person has ever loved or anyone who's loved the person, so you have to break it down even more, to the person's family of origin or his or her self-created family such as friends, colleagues, or partners.

I discovered Regina was reacting to her colleagues. When I looked for what emotion her body was responding to within the love category, I found the feeling of irritability. I asked her how she might be feeling irritable with her colleagues and she said that three years prior, her former colleagues devised lies to get her fired from her job. She felt they didn't like the fact that she was advancing even though she was relatively new at the company. Since being at her present job, she sensed a similar set up and therefore didn't feel emotionally safe and was constantly on guard.

Regina was rejected by her former job, given no recourse, and she couldn't prove that lies were being told about her. She was put in a position where legal action would have proved more costly with no guarantee of winning. She felt humiliated. Although it only took a few months to land at another company in the same position, the shock and stress she felt from being fired with no warning caused her to lose her baby.

I helped her identify various emotions associated with losing her job, such as feeling powerless, longing to be heard, helplessness, lost sense of dignity, and lost sense of inner security.

Each session consisted of using Regina's back pain as the pathway to finding what emotions she had repressed about her colleagues. Sometimes it had roots in childhood.

She described feeling misunderstood and overlooked by her parents. She always felt as though her younger brother was jealous of her and always tried to out-do her.

Remarks would leak out here and there and I made mental notes. One time she mentioned that a lot of her peers didn't expect her to be smart and pretty, which, in her mind, served to make them feel threatened by her. She further explained that when she had come into her new role, she advanced a lot faster than people who had been there much longer, much like what had happened at her old job, adding to the animosity she already felt from them.

She reiterated what she had been telling me since the first meeting, that wherever she went, women hated her and didn't make her feel welcome. She'd been unable to break the pattern and was always trying to figure out why she found herself in the same situations time and time again.

I really wanted to help Regina figure out why women were constantly undermining her, why that had been a pattern for so long. However, within a few sessions I found her to be non-compliant with exercises I recommended she do between sessions. She half-assed one exercise and ignored the rest because she felt like they weren't worth her time. She told me she already knew the outcome or understood the exercise. Therapy, according to her, had been very beneficial for other issues before the pain developed and she insisted that she'd already processed and felt the emotions I was finding; therefore, it was unnecessary to feel more.

According to Regina, she had done the work.

She was convinced that her issues were not due to repressed emotions that hadn't been processed because she already learned what she needed in therapy. Therefore, she decided that her issues were about why she kept finding herself in the same pattern of working with women who felt threatened by her. She wanted concrete tools for how to deal with those women so that she could advance despite their ill will toward her.

Over time, a psychologist can help a patient realize how they're coming across when that person is loath to consider his or her own actions, but working with this type of personality is not something on which I focus my work.

BLACK VALENTINE'S DAY

MOM DECIDED THAT DAD'S MEMORIAL service would be held a few months after his passing so that his friends could schedule it around their busy lives, but I needed to go and connect with her soon after his passing. My friend, Alexandra, picked me up from the airport. I could tell she wanted me to emote more, but I couldn't. She even told me, "Serena, it's OK to cry. You know you don't have to hide your feelings or put on a brave face for me."

The two of us have known each other since we were eleven and in sixth grade, so I can read her like a book, and vice versa. She reminded me that my dad had just died, as if I needed to hear that again in order to put things into perspective, to realize it was OK to cry in front of someone else. Believe me, I wanted to cry and let it out, but being back in Philly triggered some sort of reflex that caused me to push those feelings down, away from the surface. I was frustrated that I couldn't cry in front of one of my oldest and dearest friends, but she knew my family and she didn't push it, she just spoke to what I knew: that it would be therapeutic to let it out rather than keep it in.

Sometimes I can't hold back the tears. Other times, I can. Years of repressing my emotions taught me how to do just that. Sometimes when I'm overwhelmed and I don't know when the tears will stop, I try to hold them back because I worry that letting a few tears fall will cause the floodgates to open and I'll lose all control.

Going to Philly less than a week after my dad passed seemed like the obvious thing to do. That's what families do when they've lost family members, or so it seemed to me.

Then I got home and entered the family lair.

My visit back home coincided with Valentine's Day. In the afternoon, I spent time with my mom. I quickly fell back into my role of being Mom's therapist: listening, reflecting, but not offering my feelings or opinions. If she had offered me comfort, I don't know if anything would have come from it, if I had the capacity to feel comforted.

That evening, Graham sat across from me at the table, surrounded by his morose-looking wife and kids. On a good day, Graham and I hardly spoke to each other, let alone when someone close to us had gone and died. I didn't feel that much more connected to Layla, his wife. She glanced my way, passed me the dinner rolls, and went back to fussing over the children. Although I found Layla friendly and outgoing from the moment she was introduced to the family, I couldn't relate to her on a lot of levels because she seemed to lack ambition and chose to focus her life around Graham and raising their kids.

At the table, my mother made a comment about one of my dad's friends, what he was up to, and all of us nodded our heads. Graham took a bite of potatoes and stared ahead.

Apart from the holidays, the last time Graham and I had spent any time together was seven years prior. He and Layla had thrown a wedding party at the family house on Cape Cod a year after they eloped. They explained that the wedding party was a way to celebrate their union with their friends and family, the people who hadn't been present when they'd eloped. I'd gone out to Big Sur when Graham had informed me of his plans. I wanted to offer some moral support and to hang out in Big Sur, which was only four hours from San Francisco, where I then lived.

The wedding party at the Cape over a year later ended up looking exactly like a wedding celebration. There was a dinner the night before, a party with a band, dancing, a tent, catered food, toasts the next day, and a brunch on Sunday. The only thing missing was a ceremony.

Initially, I considered not going. But then my mom got upset with me. "Just because you went to the real wedding doesn't mean you shouldn't go to Graham's party. Why would you consider not going? It will show a lack of care and disrespect. Graham's invited a lot of people and Dad and I expect you to go."

Mom and weddings. This was her arena to see and be seen, show off her kids.

When I complained to my friends, they offered to be my dates. Layla told me I could bring whomever I wanted so I did just that. Family from the West Coast attended, and I brought three of my favorite gay friends at the time.

I flew in from San Francisco and met my friends in New York City and we drove to the Cape. I wanted my friends to be aware of how mean Graham could be to me and how, in order to avoid his toxicity, I shut off from feeling around him. I wanted them to understand what was wrong with me, to know that my lack of emotional capacity had nothing to do with them, and everything to do with my need to self-protect. I didn't know how to guard against Graham and keep my heart open to my close friends, so I wanted them to get this connection.

On the way to Cape Cod, I warned them so they would understand my desire for their protection. They assured me that my dynamics were not uncommon and they chalked it up to sibling rivalry. They bent over backwards to make me feel normal, even though I feared I was anything but.

When we got to the Cape, the four of us walked through the front door and there was Graham. He hadn't seen us arrive, so it was happenstance that he was right there at the entrance.

"Hello, Graham."

"Hello, Serena."

Silence. A pregnant silence filled the air for almost a minute while Graham and I locked eyes, stared at each other. Neither of us said anything else.

My friends were so stunned that their jaws dropped. They had never seen siblings greet each other this way. No one knew what to do with the tension, until Drew (not the same chatty Cathy) introduced himself in a relaxed way, offering polite chit-chat with an Australian-accented twist. Eventually, we all made our way in to meet my other relatives.

For the rest of the weekend and for years afterwards, my friends would say, "Hello, Graham. Hello, Serena," to replay and rehash the hollow and detached relationship I have with my brother.

My friends made the visit to the Cape so much more enjoyable than if I had gone on my own. They teased me and asked why I hadn't invited them to the house before. They were having a blast with all the amenities and activities to be had, including swimming and tennis. They made being around my family that much easier just by being themselves and providing a buffer.

After a night of dancing and drinking and staying up late, we were all sleeping soundly in our room (the one we almost didn't secure because Graham wanted it for Layla's family, telling me we could find a hotel). Graham barged in, he didn't even knock, and demanded that we move our car. "Serena! Your friend's car is blocking Layla's uncle's car. You have to move it. He can't get out."

Startled, we slowly got to our feet, but apparently not fast enough for Graham. "Serena! Move the car now. Not in ten minutes. Now."

Once Graham slammed the door, my friend, whose car we had taken for the trip, looked at me and said, "Your brother's an asshole. We seriously thought you were exaggerating but it's been clear since we arrived and now we know why you tried to warn us."

If my friends came for nothing else than to witness the treatment I received from Graham and to confirm that I had not been fabricating his behavior, the trip was a success.

I tried for years to improve our relationship; I really did. I sent him books that I thought might interest him. I made an attempt to connect him with my friends. Apart from reluctantly letting me stay with him in New York City for my three-week internship at *Spirituality & Health* magazine, due to my mom's pressure, he never did anything to ameliorate things between us.

When he was working for a start-up that was expanding to San Francisco, he came to visit. I'd been living there less than a year. I took him to meet my friend Kyle, another grad student studying psychology, in the heart of the Castro. When I left for a few minutes, Kyle and Graham were left to converse on their own. Out of everyone I knew, I trusted Kyle would know how to talk to Graham and not get frustrated with how sarcastic and obnoxious he can be. When I returned, it appeared that they were getting along swimmingly.

Kyle later told me that within sixty seconds of me leaving, with no prompting from him, Graham blurted out, "I know Serena resents me. I know I wasn't nice to her growing up. She resents me for the way I treated her when we were little just like the way I resent my dad for the way he treated me when I was growing up."

Despite Graham's insights into our contentious relationship, we never became close.

Despite my best efforts, Graham would often fly off the handle when things didn't go his way and lash out at me. While on break for the Christmas holiday during my junior year of college, I wanted to use the car to go Christmas shopping. But Graham wanted to use the car to see his friends. He had already used it earlier that day, which is why I hadn't done my shopping. "Serena! You are the most bitter person I have ever known. Have you ever considered anyone but yourself for one second? What's wrong with you? You can use the car tomorrow." That should be in all caps, like just about everything else that came out of his mouth, because he was yelling at me when he said it.

That same Christmas, Graham decided to tell me how stupid I was for insisting on using alternative therapies to treat the arthritis. "Serena, you're doing yourself a disservice by not trying any medications. There are new ones on the market that could help you. It's been eleven years since you were diagnosed. What's wrong with you that you don't try one of the newer meds? Have you tried Vioxx? It's one of the newer ones and you haven't even heard of it. Why are you being so stubborn about even researching the treatment options?"

Although, it may seem like he cared and wanted me to feel better, in typical Graham fashion, he sounded hostile and condescending, like he was the expert on my issues and I was the nitwit for not taking prescription medication.

"Graham! There is no medication on the market right now that reverses arthritis. Whatever is available is there to manage the symptoms and they come with a lot of side effects. I'm the one with the condition and I've figured out how to feel better when pain happens. You have no experience with pain like this or trying to feel better so don't tell me what to do when you don't know."

My mom decided to chime in, take Graham's side like she often did without considering how it would affect me, or so it seemed.

"Honey, Graham is right. Why don't you at least try the medication he suggested. You might end up feeling better."

The trouble with trying to fight back, particularly with someone like Graham, is that I would exert energy—mental and emotional—that would only drain me. He continued putting me down, only seeing his side. That's how some of us stop fighting; we stop trying to put something right, to connect. Even if it turned out he was wrong, I would never get an apology.

When Vioxx ended up killing a lot of people, I asked my mom if she was still interested in taking his side. She'd come to his defense no matter what and Graham never offered anything in the way of admitting he was wrong.

In the days right after my dad passed, my mom told me

Graham had been a big help. He figured out how to bypass my dad's password and access his cell phone so that he could find any messages or emails that needed to be returned, contact those that should be informed of the news. I felt criticized by her somehow, as though she were insinuating that Graham, who lived only forty-five minutes away, could easily come over and help, whereas I, the elusive one, was hiding out all the way across the country, six hours away by plane. Useless, selfish Serena.

Yet, as we gathered after Dad's death, Graham hardly talked to anyone at the table, absorbed in his own world, just like always. I tried to decide if my mom felt consoled by his presence or by mine. It was hard to tell with her.

Sitting on the couch after dinner, I realized I'd gone home to be with my family and yet it wasn't comforting in the least. Instead, it was stressful. We were a bunch of strangers circling each other like planets, never really connecting or talking about anything that mattered, like feelings. I thought it would feel right to be around my family, but it didn't seem to make a difference. Although I suppose, on some level, more subconsciously than anything, it may have allowed me to normalize my tendency to repress. After all, since everyone around me was not showing emotion, it would seem more out of place if I did.

I made the trip for nothing. Dad was dead, and that was all there was to it.

When Mom dropped Glinda and I off at the airport to return to Seattle, Mom got out and gave me a hug, still the C-type hug where we don't truly touch bodies. She looked like she was on the verge of tears.

"I love you, Mom."

"I know." She didn't want to say anything more because

she was on the verge of crying, so we left it at that.

That was the third time I've said those words to her. She has never said them back. I asked her about it once and she told me that they're just words. According to her, actions speak louder than words. After a while, I started believing her, buying into her schtick. I found it mundane whenever I overheard a friend give their parents the quick, "I love you," before hanging up. They'd been on the phone all of two minutes, but still ended the call that way. To my ears, it didn't sound genuine. If you say something all the time it tends to lose its meaning. At least that's how I saw things.

Three months later, in May, the weather was warmer and we were all back at the farm in New Hope, outside of Philly, for Dad's service. I spoke, so did Graham, my uncle, and three prominent attorneys who had been his close friends.

My mom planned to spread Dad's ashes in one of the fields the day after the service. This was the reason why his service was in May not February. Although, it also made sense to postpone the ceremony for a few months after his passing so all his friends could plan their visit. He counted amongst his friends busy and important people.

My mom wanted to spread Dad's ashes in the presence of immediate family only; she didn't even want her grandkids there, assuming they wouldn't comprehend what was going on and might misbehave. Of course, Graham's kids acted like children, played with a tennis ball, thinking it was all fun. They were too young to understand how the bag full of ashes used to be their grandpa. My mom was trying to get them to focus or get Graham or Layla to take control of their kids, while at the same time staying present with spreading her husband's ashes. At one point, as we read different poems, I tried to comfort her by putting my arm around her shoulders, but it felt so awkward I stopped. I wanted to feel safe, to let myself cry and really feel and allow the emotions to come up and out; but of all people, the members of my family are the ones with whom I feel the least comfortable.

CLIENT CASE:
CYNTHIA

CYNTHIA WAS A BEAUTIFUL SEVENTY-YEAR-OLD married woman who presented with incontinence. She sought the help of various medical specialists who had done numerous tests, and no one could diagnose the cause of the problem. For six months prior to our meeting, Cynthia had gradually been unable to control her bladder. It was becoming so bad that she began wearing adult diapers. She didn't have any answers from doctors, and was beginning to lose hope. When Cynthia became depressed and suicidal, her daughter stepped in and suggested finding someone who treated the mind and the body.

In our first session, I had her think about her bladder. Using muscle testing, I found that she was weak in the category of love. For Cynthia, her muscle went weak when testing her family of origin and when looking for a specific person, I found her body was responding to her father.

Next, I identified the emotion of grief. When I asked Cynthia to explain how she might feel grief in connection to her father, she burst into tears. She explained that her daddy, as she referred to him, was killed in a car accident when she was a little girl. She had been close to him and the shock and grief that accompanied his sudden passing never left her. In pulling out more emotions her body had stored, I found the feeling of resentment and anger. I asked her how she connected those feelings with her dad's accident, thinking those are common feelings to experience after the death of a loved one. However, her body responded more to the relationship that changed with her mother. Her mother was not soft, warm, and empathetic. She demanded perfection, even berating Cynthia for getting her dress dirty on one occasion when she climbed trees with her friends.

Cynthia never felt like she could make her mother proud of her. With her dad, Cynthia could be a child, but with her mother, she had to be prim and proper and always do one hundred and ten percent.

In subsequent sessions, I found feelings of being stifled and an inability to express her complaints. These feelings, left over from her childhood, now had to do with her current work environment. Cynthia explained that within the past year, she had taken a job with a very taxing medical doctor. She initially signed on to do his medical billing but when his secretary quit, she took over that role, too. Soon enough, she had taken on the job of other employees who had also quit in response to the doctor's unrealistic demands. They had all become so stressed they couldn't take it anymore. Soon enough, Cynthia was doing the job of five people without being compensated or acknowledged for all her work. Instead of saying anything, she kept her feelings to herself, assuming the doctor would realize he needed to hire replacements, but he never did.

After the first session, Cynthia reported that she only

had incontinence seven times a day which was a huge relief since the issue had become so bad that she was "going" up to twenty times a day. She also felt comforted in knowing that there was an intervention that was helping her. I continued to see her and help her process the sadness from losing her dad as well as the other unacknowledged emotions she felt with regards to her mom. Within a few months the incontinence went away.

As she recognized the similarities between her boss and her taskmaster mother, she realized that no amount of sacrifice would satisfy her boss just like nothing was ever good enough for her mother. She eventually quit and created her own business as a medical biller for individual doctors. She carved out an office in her home, made her own hours, and made sure to practice self-care as she developed her new business.

BAD BRA

Aunt Jenny's passing came as a shock. After arriving in Boston the day before I learned the news, I thought of texting my cousin, Polly, while waiting in the ridiculous hour-and-a-half line for the rental car, but for some reason I didn't. I texted her the following morning after I arrived at my Airbnb. I was curious to see if she had any suggestions on neighborhoods to explore.

Her reply to my text blindsided me.

"Serena. My mom passed away last night." I sat down on the bed, trying to grasp and comprehend what I just read. It was an awful feeling that threatened to spread through my body.

"What? I'm so sorry." I didn't know how to make sense of the news.

"I'm sorry. I just can't read your message." She paused in her typing for a moment. "Sorry to tell you on text."

I sat on the bed stunned. I was getting ready to have a session with a past life regression hypnotherapist located forty-five minutes away, but I was flooded with emotion and I wasn't sure what I should do. Although I hadn't seen Aunt Jenny for five years, she was often on my mind or mentioned in conversation. Polly had just mentioned her to me the week before. Then I did what I always did, placed the unpleasant feelings on the back burner.

I had planned to see Cliff, the past life regression therapist, for over a month. I had heard him interviewed on a podcast I enjoyed listening to: *The Paranormal Podcast*. I thought perhaps I could get answers for why I have yet to find my mate, why my friends have all dated, married, divorced, and remarried in the time I've spent pursuing relationships that never lasted longer than six months. Surely there was some other reason besides not knowing how to pick the right guys.

Why, I wondered, had Uncle Frank and Aunt Jenny found each other and spent more than fifty years together while others, like myself, spend years looking for that one special person? It was a comforting idea that there was some other force at work preventing me from finding and having a love relationship. It's easier to think the cause is "out there" rather than the sign of some fatal flaw on my part.

Despite lacking discernment for allowing narcissistic men into my life, I have a bullshit meter that I've been able to trust. I've met a number of alternative healers who have suggested things that are completely dubious. I can spot these people because they come from ego, boastful of what they think they know all the while being completely off base. I connected with a supposed psychic a few years ago who told me I was yearning for a family, suggesting I couldn't wait to have kids. When I interrupted him and told him I've never wanted kids he took offense and told me I must be in denial of my own desires because he's never been wrong. Fortunately for both of us, he stopped the session soon after that interaction and refunded me my money.

For the very same reason people seek a psychotherapist or life coach, I look to other types of healers for answers. Perhaps there's something I'm not seeing about how I view relationships or why I keep attracting the wrong matches. Psychologists help their patients break the cycle of behaving, feeling, and thinking the same way, which keeps them stuck. While I've been trained in traditional psychotherapy, I find the process of exploring such areas, oftentimes ad nauseuam, to be incredibly slow. After learning and implementing more mind body techniques into my practice and watching my clients transform within a few sessions, I no longer had the patience as a client myself, to uncover, over many months or years, what I couldn't see. I was much more open to exploring past life regression therapy or another type of healing approach.

I had done a past life regression two years before. In it I explored only one past life. I was a woman in the 1960s who'd gotten married young, in her twenties, had a loving family, and had a rewarding career as well. The takeaway lesson, the one the practitioner teased out with me: even though my brother can often be so mean and uncaring, and even though I don't feel close to my immediate family, it doesn't mean that everyone is out to get me. I just need to distinguish who to trust and let in since I learned not to let my guard down with my family members. In short, I am capable of being a member of a loving family.

When I arrived at Cliff's office, I was armed with a question that had been haunting me since that first past life session. Was I daydreaming and creating those memories or were they really past lives I was exploring?

He asked me if I felt as though I was an analytical person.

"Well, I have a doctorate in clinical psychology and tend to think deeply about most everything so, yes, I'd say I'm pretty analytical."

Cliff didn't say anything in response to this, so I guess analytical people are harder to hypnotize. They overthink things and doubt the process, ask questions other people just accept at face value. The problem is, I can't just be a patient, I have to analyze a practitioner's clinical approach—figure out why they go about doing what they do, what they're going after in a roundabout way.

I've found in my own practice that some clients are skeptical of the techniques I use. I know what they're thinking: *If it's not a talk-it-out approach, will the practitioner be able to fool me?* I had one client tell me that he outsmarted all of his other therapists and he really needed help. He was desperate to make amends with his girlfriend, but he was worried that my treatment wouldn't work because he knew how to answer the therapist's questions in a way that would put him in the best light. He was concerned that he would somehow do that with me.

Other clients have also asked if they have to possess certain spiritual beliefs in order for my treatments to work. In both cases, I have explained that it doesn't matter whether they believe it will work or not, I'm making a change to their physiology by finding the emotion that is inhibiting them from moving forward. Once we identify that emotion and make the connection as to why they feel the way they do regarding their issue, they are able to feel better mentally, emotionally, and physically.

Likewise, with the client who was concerned he could outsmart me, I clarified that as astute as I'd like to think I am, and as sharp as he may be, the techniques bypass the rational brain, the part of the brain that thinks before it speaks. In traditional therapy, he would have time to consider the question, formulate different responses, and as a result, not be present with the emotions arising—he would be able to deflect them and thereby not truly feel. Working with me would be different. I told him that I used manual muscle testing as a way to ask the body for answers; by doing so, I get right to the issue. I always try to build rapport so the client feels emotionally safe when feelings spill out without control.

So, back to mixing my experiences as a patient and as a practitioner. I totally got where my clever client was coming from. I was the same way in my own psychotherapy sessions; I rarely emoted. I was always in control. When I hire alternative practitioners to use their techniques for my issues, I can't always predict how I will react and that's where the healing happens. I need the element of surprise. I need exactly what Cliff was employing; to get at the trouble from unexpected angles before I could throw up a roadblock.

Growing up I learned to hold my feelings in no matter what, regardless of whether my body would later develop pain. At least I wouldn't be seen as weak to my family. So even when I'm the client and tears pour down my face as a result of pinpointing the issue, it's still uncomfortable. But I would much prefer figuring out the issue rather than skirting around the problem and being able to convince the therapist of whatever I wanted so I wouldn't have to confront the real issue. That dance got old; I tired of it as a practitioner and as a client.

I didn't find much out about any past life, so Cliff decided to do some hypnotherapy about becoming more discernible, about letting the right people in, and kicking out the toxic ones before they wreaked havoc on my life.

Maybe it's easier to get through this life by not feeling deeply, not getting attached to someone the way Uncle Frank was to Aunt Jenny because then I won't hurt the way he did at that moment. Their relationship, at least from the outside, seemed so deeply loving, which makes me think his loss will feel that much worse. And maybe this is what I've feared all along, letting someone in, then suffering in the face of their loss, especially since I learned how to detach and not feel. If I were to truly experience the extent of feelings for another, perhaps I would be devastated and unable to cope if something were to happen to him.

I discovered past lives through NET, even before the one I mentioned. One made a lot of sense to me and deeply resonated. I was a woman living in France during one of the wars two lifetimes ago. My husband died in the war and I was so upset I killed myself. There it is again, the fear of losing someone I truly love. Better to have never loved at all than to have lost. Those feelings—the amplified fear of loss, not knowing how to recover from the end of a relationship where I fully let myself be seen and heard, armor off—those seemed more pronounced than normal. It was why I wondered whether a past life was still working through my present one. Perhaps I hadn't fully healed from a trauma from a previous life because I killed myself or my life was somehow cut short before I could process what I needed to and thus, all the heartache and fear was still in me.

It brings to mind a TV series I used to watch with Graham growing up—The Hardy Boys. Only one episode truly stuck, for years and years after watching it. In it, the younger Hardy boy had finally found his One and Only. They drove off in a convertible sports car after their wedding ceremony and crashed into another car that cut them off. The Hardy boy survived, but his beautiful new bride was killed.

He was mortified. I wanted no part of that anguish.

Of course, now that my father is dead, my mother is alone. Devastation after loss isn't part of her makeup, at least as far as she lets on. I've got to think that, after the initial shock of losing her husband, she had to feel some sense of freedom. He was a difficult man who put her down and stifled many of her ambitions. And what do I know? They may well have been products of their era where women were supposed to make a good home for their husbands, make all the meals, clean, parent, and listen to the man as if his life held more weight than any dream or aspiration she held.

"If I had died first," she said on more than one occasion, "you know Dad would have found some young honey, probably not much older than you." I suppose this was her way of suggesting that he wouldn't have mourned her. Or perhaps she was suggesting that Dad would have been unable to take care of himself and would have married soon after her death so that he would have a woman to take care of him—make his meals, do his laundry, listen to him without him giving much in return. Maybe she said it to make it OK that she didn't demonstrate grief, or perhaps she felt more for him and theirs was a lopsided relationship. It certainly seemed unbalanced from my perspective. Why they even stayed together, I will never know. Though I suppose they were on the same page in many ways. Maybe my parents were on to something. Fuck the whole soulmate thing; marry someone you can work with who shares your same values. At least then, if I lost my partner, I would be able to carry on and not feel an overwhelming hole in my heart the way I imagined I would if my soulmate met me on a deeper emotional level.

The problem with this scenario: it isn't fulfilling. I've become so comfortable with my own company that I don't feel the need to settle down just to have companionship. Since I don't get lonely and I don't need a partner to help with finances, the desire to find someone comes down to love. But how do you find someone to love, someone who can love you when you feel perpetually emotionally detached?

After the past life regression session with Cliff, I met up with Julie, a friend I've known since grad school in San Francisco, who lives in New Hampshire. We connected in Rockport, a quaint seaside town off the coast of Massachusetts about an hour north of Boston. I was still thinking about my aunt's death in the back of my mind. At some point during our wanderings, my chest started hurting. I couldn't figure out why. For the lack of any other reason, I figured it was due to my underwire bra. I didn't wear that bra much, which seemed like a plausible enough excuse for chest pain. Although, when I thought about it, the pain was only in one spot on the left side of my chest. If it wasn't my underwire then perhaps a rib was out. How a rib got out of alignment I couldn't fathom. At the time, I couldn't imagine why it felt like I'd bruised my chest. This whole analysis played out in my mind as we strolled the streets and popped in and out of stores. Leave it to my body to create a new problem.

Polly asked if I would stop by that day, so after spending a few hours with Julie, I drove to Frank's. Polly, her husband, and her kids had gathered as well as a number of Frank and Jenny's friends. It was then that it dawned on me: it wasn't so much my chest that hurt but my heart. The pain wasn't because of my bra, or a popped rib, or a bruise of some sort, but because of the shock and sadness I felt about Jenny's sudden passing. All the back-burner stuff, the emotions I'd stuffed because they weren't convenient, shifted right to the front.

How was I supposed to make sense of death, of a loss like that, most of all for Frank? How do people go on? How would Frank carry on? Polly and the rest?

I wasn't in Philadelphia right after my dad passed. I was in Seattle. It was a week before I visited my mom and when I did, I found the kitchen full of cards and flowers. Neighbors had brought over food but there wasn't a constant influx of friends and family the way there was at Frank's. Even when I visited Frank a month later, friends and colleagues were stopping by to check on him, talk with him, and see how he was holding up.

Did my mom lose the love of her life or was their relationship a working one that made the loss less difficult? I don't know the answer to that. What I do know is that my mom rarely showed sadness. Even after my dad died, at times it looked like she might let the tears come down her face, but she held it together. The day after Aunt Jenny died suddenly, Frank was sitting in his living room, surrounded by friends and family, and he didn't hold back. He cried in front of them about the shock and grief that was overwhelming; he wasn't embarrassed to let his loved ones see his display of pain. I never saw my mom show her grief not even when she was spreading my dad's ashes.

I know Polly's relationship to Aunt Jenny wasn't always easy. It was even more complicated with my cousin Max, Jenny's other child. But what made Aunt Jenny's passing different than what I experienced when my dad passed was that Polly, Max, and Frank all talked openly to each other about their grief. They didn't try to put on a brave face. It was that outward acceptance of sadness and loss, their open communication of it even if it looked and felt messy that was antithetical to what I experienced in my own family.

Loss is an inevitable part of life. Perhaps it's because I lacked a proper model for mourning and recovery that made the thought of it unbearable.

It's good to cry and let it out rather than keep everything inside so no one can see. First, open grief is appropriate and healthy. Second, which I've only recently come to realize, people feel closer to you when you show emotions—even the not-so-pretty ones.

I can talk all I want about my mom but being at Frank's place really showed me how detached and emotionally isolated I was when Dad passed. Not only was I in a new city when I'd learned of his death (where I had yet to make close friends), my own family felt useless in the support department. Weren't they supposed to make things feel better? I grieved after Dad passed but the big difference was that I felt alone in my grieving even when I went "home" to Philadelphia to be with my family. No one comforted me. But was I supposed to comfort Mom? I still ask myself that question. I tried by listening and offering to make the meals and take care of the dogs. She refused to let me and was more comfortable doing those things herself. Maybe I didn't know how to be of comfort to her, in much the same way that she didn't know how to soothe me.

I studied my uncle in the midst of his support network. It was heart-warming to see a constant flow of people around Frank, people who cared, who came to be with him as soon as they learned the horrible news. I watched Frank interact with his friends. Even if I had close friends around in Seattle when my father died, I don't know that I would have known how to accept their help, not the way Frank did. How did Frank turn out so warm, loving, and caring while Dad was anything but? Frank is a good man.

Which leads me to wonder . . .

Is it better to go through life having a working relationship with a partner, a companion? Am I incapable, or just too afraid of what it would mean to lose him?

THE CASE OF JOSÉ FERNANDEZ

As is often the case, it wasn't until after José Fernandez tragically died that I took interest in his story. I'm not sure I was even aware of this young and extremely talented baseball player when he was alive. His rags-to-riches story of defecting from Cuba wasn't the bit that grabbed my attention. Rather, it was the immense love he felt for and from his mother and grandmother that caused me to feel such grief in the days following his death.

I cried for days. I didn't know what had come over me. Julie thought I must have been triggered and was remembering the pain of grieving Dad's death, but it didn't feel like that was it. I couldn't stop crying so I finally made an appointment to see my NET chiropractor. During my session, I discovered that I had become emotional because the love José Fernandez had from and for his family reflected the lack I felt from my own.

The baseball player overcame such odds and had his whole life ahead of him yet, just like that, it was cut short. He was just twenty-four years old, with a promising future ahead of him and a family who adored him, when he died in a boating accident that could have been prevented had he made smarter choices.

Beyond the grief I felt, I wondered how much of his success was due to the unwavering love his family gave and instilled in him. He grew up in Cuba, in a house in which he shared his room with his grandmother, who taught him to play baseball. Some days he would find some branches and use them to hit around a ball.

On his third attempt to defect from Cuba, he heard someone fall in the water and yell for help. Without thinking, he dove in to save the person. Turned out, he saved his mom's life. Once he arrived in Florida, where he met up with his dad, he sold vegetables on the side of the road for a few dollars a day to make money. His English wasn't great, so he struggled in high school, but he had a passion and talent for baseball. He found a coach who was relentless in getting José to practice as much as possible. It paid off. The Marlins scouted him right out of high school.

Here's what grabbed my professional attention: Only one year into his professional baseball career, he injured his arm, as many pitchers do, and required Tommy John surgery, a procedure to repair his torn ulnar collateral ligament. This is an anxiety-provoking surgery for many players because the operation carries with it the risk that they won't get better, they'll grow worse. Some players don't return to one hundred percent.

José's case was interesting to me on a professional level as well. When athletes get injured or develop acute or chronic pain, they want to get relief as soon as possible. They don't just want to feel better. They also want to get back to their game, otherwise their careers may be over.

When the pressure to succeed is so great, it's often easier to point to physical pain and use it as an excuse to not participate. Like the baseball player who can't cope with being the hometown favorite, so he has one injury or illness after another which gives him an out. This doesn't happen consciously. It might start as anxiety; but if not addressed, it can develop into physical issues. Symptoms let people justify why they're not performing optimally. Thinking positive thoughts, saying affirmations, using breath work, meditation, and visualization are all helpful but those are cognitive interventions and they won't address the cause of someone's presenting issue if it's something they're not aware of.

And yet, José returned better than he was before the surgery. During rehab, he followed his doctors' instructions, did what he was told, and despite not being able to play and compete with his team, he came to all their practices and games. He was disciplined in his rehab.

I wondered whether he recuperated so well as a result of being so supported and loved by his family.

NO FILTER

A FEW YEARS AGO, I was getting my period three times a month. After consulting with numerous alternative healers, I finally sought (Western) medical intervention and went for tests, all of which came up negative. On one visit, the nurse practitioner suggested that I might have some sort of cancer in the cervix or ovaries.

At first, I was sad, mainly because this nurse's bedside manner was awful, just like the nurse six years prior who left a message on my voicemail informing me that I needed to get extra tests because she was concerned I had cervical cancer—all matter-of-fact, as if ordering what she wanted to eat off a menu. When I'd gone for a follow-up visit back then, I told the nurse, a short woman who reminded me of Yoda (in appearance only, as she lacked his wisdom), that I did not appreciate her voicemail because it came off as completely devoid of empathy. Not surprisingly, she was defensive. I didn't bother informing the more recent nurse that her bedside manner needed improvement.

On the way home, my sadness turned to relief. Some people pray for health; I have done the opposite. I've prayed for a fast-acting terminal illness to take me out; or I've hoped to be in a fatal accident—preferably one where Glinda and I get to go together, and where death is pain-free and immediate. Of course, dying peacefully in my sleep would be ideal, but since when does that ever happen?

If it really was cancer, I would keep the news to myself. Slowly, my health would decline, and I wouldn't tell anyone. Perhaps I'd be in pain, but eventually, I'd get to depart from this world and I could blame it on cancer. It seemed a lot more acceptable than taking my own life.

With arthritis, what I wanted was attention; underneath that, there was the desire to be seen and heard and not feel second best to Graham. With cancer, I wanted to be free of emotional pain. Whether I move on to some afterlife where I learn from my life on Earth and progress my soul forward, or whether there is nothing and I cease to have any consciousness, death often seems more desirable than the sadness and frustration I feel by being alive. But taking one's own life seems less noble than dying from some illness that doctors can't cure. Suicide is giving up. I've also been worried that if consciousness does continue and I take my own life that I'll end up in some no man's land, unable to delight in all the good things, or so I've read, that will greet us when we pass on to the other side. Everyone tells you, "Life will get better." I've been taught how to save people from suicidal ideations. Cancer is something that befalls you, even if you're healthy and many people recover. Some don't.

Depression, and that's what lies beneath my romantic cancer fantasy, doesn't discriminate between rich or poor, old or young. There are statistics that suggest that the elderly are more likely to kill themselves than any other population and it makes sense. Most older people have lost loved ones, spouses, friends. Their children have moved away. They're in ill health, experiencing things like incontinence, which forces them into diapers. They might be homebound due to poor health. Many wind up in an assisted living center, having some nurse wipe their ass because they're too feeble to do basic tasks anymore. That sounds downright depressing to me and in that situation, I'd pay someone to smother me with a pillow.

You don't have to be old and ailing to want to off yourself. Kate Spade and Anthony Bourdain died in the same week, both from suicide, both by hanging. Kate and Anthony built extremely successful careers for themselves from the ground up and yet they couldn't escape the torment of their own minds. That's what can happen when you're depressed; you end up putting a rope around your neck.

Then there are people like me. Youngish, not famous. To many people looking at me, I suppose I appear to have it all: I'm highly educated, I have a promising career, I've lived in a number of cosmopolitan cities abroad and in the US, my finances allow me to not stress about food or housing, and I'm privileged to be white in the US. Even though I have arthritis, it's not crippling. So, what would make someone like me feel depressed?

My depression isn't constant. It seems I turned a corner after turning forty and I don't fall prey to depressive states the way I used to. But when I feel it, I plummet. It's not just feeling sad for a few hours or a day. One negative thought spills into a deeper abyss and before I know it, I'm convinced my life will never get better, that I'm damaged. Because I've been disconnecting from feelings since I was little, I'll never be able to change or develop fulfilling emotional connections that allow me to feel love; so, essentially, I'd be better off dead.

Just like the arthritis, I taught myself how not to feel, but I did such a good job, I made it impossible to feel connected and close to anyone else even if they're good for me. Imagining that I'll never be able to feel beyond the hard wall I built around myself and considering that my life will only continue to be one in which I'm detached from my emotions feels hopeless. I brought it upon myself just like I created arthritis and yet I feel stuck. Even with Apartment Boy, although my body felt the effects of being heard, seen, and loved by him, much of the time when we were dating, I asked myself why I couldn't feel more for him and from him.

In order to graduate from my doctoral program, I had to go through my own therapy. As you remember, before that, my experience with therapy consisted of two dreadful experiences, one while I was in high school and the other while working in New York City. I chose to fulfill my requirement by seeing a few different therapists so I could experience different approaches. For instance, how was psychodynamic therapy different from humanistic therapy? I tried to be the patient but I would also be in observer mode, assessing the therapist for how he or she spoke to me. Did I feel they really cared or were they trying to cover their butts and excuse themselves from liability when I expressed suicidal thoughts?

I would never agree to no-harm contracts or, on the rare occasion that I did, I would tell the therapist, "I'll make one so you're not libel, but if I want to kill myself I'm going to do it anyway. A contract means nothing especially when you're dead." No one wants to be talked out of suicide when they've convinced themselves it's the best move for them.

I was not a good patient. I knew too much, having the training myself. Instead of a no-harm contract, it seemed the more caring offer would be to tell a patient that if they're feeling suicidal, to contact them, their therapist. Why tell them to call a hotline and talk to a stranger when it's the therapist who has been listening to them all along?

Asking me to identify and explain my feelings when I wasn't even sure what it was that I was feeling put me right back in my head, intellectualizing rather than sitting with the difficult emotions causing my sadness. I could rationalize and make sense of why I was upset. That sometimes gave me some resolve; it was as if knowing there was a cause for my emotional pain allowed me to realize there were reasons for my depressive thoughts and I didn't have some faulty brain wiring. But it didn't alleviate the sadness. It often made me feel worse, which I learned was normal. Sitting in your muck doesn't always help you feel better right away, but with consistent effort, you get on the other side of depressive thoughts and feelings.

Just as the earlier therapists had, the therapists I saw during my required fifty-five hours always made me feel like they had all the answers, but they weren't going to give them to me because I had to learn them on my own. I understood the rationale behind that. You can't fully understand something if someone tells you what's going on. You have to feel it yourself. But it still bugged me that I felt similar to some of my patients who had dementia: progress was incredibly slow. When you're depressed, you want to feel better quickly. You don't want to take months to feel the same or worse. Maybe that's just me.

Speaking of hotlines. I've been on the other side of the hotline, fielding calls from elderly patients asking me what they have to live for. I've secretly agreed with them that they had a pretty bleak life and if I were them, I'd feel exactly the same. But my training taught me to save lives when someone is emotionally tormented rather than agree. Thank God I have more sense than the cervical cancer nurses.

Therapy aside, I've learned to keep everything to myself especially when I'm sad and depressed. When I finally had the courage to tell Mom I was so depressed, she laughed it off. And I stopped telling her when I was in physical pain because she gave me sympathy, which accentuated that I had a disability. Sympathy makes me feel weak, like there's something really wrong with me. It feels like I'm somehow flawed and certainly not equal to whoever is doling out the sympathy.

It's still not socially acceptable to talk about depression. When I'm in the thick of it, I keep to myself, withdraw from friends, and give some vague excuse like, "I've got to catch up on work." I know I can talk to a close friend and sometimes all it takes is getting some perspective and realizing that everything I was thinking that made me feel sad and hopeless was just thoughts. Thoughts aren't facts, but we have the ability to make them feel that way.

When I do talk about my depressive thoughts, first I have to make sure that the person I'm talking to won't judge me or be dismissive. My family informed me that my feelings didn't matter so what I want is for someone to listen without having answers that sound like a Hallmark card or a quote from Pinterest that will make everything better. Julie is really helpful in this department. She reflects back to me what I'm thinking and feeling and asks questions that make me curious about why I'm feeling the way I am and helps me consider other alternatives.

One of the first things I learned in grad school was that just because I've experienced arthritis or depression, doesn't make me know how someone else feels who also has these conditions. It feels incredibly dismissive and the other person comes off as completely presumptuous when they tell me, "I know how you feel." I have a friend who will often tell me those very words and I've shot back and told her she doesn't. "No, you don't know how I feel, because you are not me!" She gets upset but she, like many people, feels better about herself when she thinks she's helping by assuming to know how I feel. In fact, it's completely unhelpful.

Many people don't know how to listen without fixing and solving another person's problem. It's as if we've learned that we have to make it better for each other so instead of reflecting back and letting someone process their emotions, we come up with solutions.

I used to be able to flip a switch and decide not to feel but it meant my body would be in pain instead. I realize why it felt better to be in physical pain: the alternative—emotional pain—was much harder for me to deal with. The shame, sadness, hopelessness, anger, and sense of failure was much more burdensome than coping with joint pain. Not being able to turn off my feelings shows progress. It reflects years of unlearning the learned reflex of shutting down emotionally.

Years ago, I got hooked on watching Vampire Diaries, a TV series surely created for a teen audience. All the actors were gorgeous and there was something oddly compelling about understanding how vampires functioned. From watching that show, I learned that I was just like a vampire. In the first season, Jeremy, one of the humans, asked Damon, the hot vampire, "They say that vampires don't have to feel pain. That they can turn it off. They shut out their humanity. Is it easier that way?"

Damon replied, "Life sucks either way. At least as a vampire you don't have to feel bad about it if you don't want to. I did it for a very long time and life was a lot easier."

CONCLUSION

IF I WERE TO TELL most medical doctors that I created juvenile rheumatoid arthritis, I'd be laughed at and told I was delusional. To their way of thinking, that's simply not how the body and mind work.

"You can't create illness," they'd likely tell me. "Just like you can't make yourself well using your mind." No, that would put them out of business and that's anathema to everything they've been taught. They've bought the same bill of goods sold to the masses, who've been brainwashed to believe that they are limited and must depend on outside sources for their health and happiness. (We could talk "fault" here, but why bother?)

If people would realize just how powerful they are, how influential their subconscious mind is, it would drastically change how they think about health, illness, and healing.

Think about it: How do people with Dissociative Identity Disorder (formerly known as Multiple Personality Disorder) change eye colors depending on which identity they're embodying at a given time? They're not consciously doing it but it's happening, nonetheless. That right there is proof that it's possible to change our physiology with our thoughts and beliefs.

I mean, how are some women able to lift a car and pull their trapped baby from beneath it? One day, they can only lift thirty pounds at the gym, the next, they're lifting a car, which weighs a few thousand pounds. The fact that it's a possibility speaks to the incredible power available within us all, one that's powered by love.

If I told the average medical doctor that love could heal pain, if I told him that repressed emotions were at the root of many pain issues (not to mention love issues), they'd look at me like I was a loon.

Now, where should I go first, to love as the antidote to pain, or to repressed emotions, because they're all intertwined?

I've spent a lot of time writing about love, my search for it as a possible cure for my chronic pain. I'm not the only one who believes that the lack of love, the associated sense of being unheard and unseen, can cause physical symptoms and that the experience of love can reverse those symptoms. Maybe it was Mister Rogers who planted that seed in my head when I was young. He said, "Love is at the root of everything, all learning, all relationships, love or the lack of it."

What I do know, from experience, is that when I feel connected to someone whom I can trust, who values me for me, not for what I do or what I have, who hears me without an ear on fulfilling their own needs, my nervous system calms down to such a degree that I feel whole and happy and that translates to less pain and tension. The safer I feel expressing my feelings, the better off my body feels. The more comfortable I am with being authentic because I'm accepted for who I am, the stronger the possibility for connection and even love. With that, I am less likely to feel like an outsider, skimming across the surface so I don't fall too far and suffer hurt.

There are all sorts of chemicals that fire in the brain when someone's in love. The bottom line is that this sense of connection, where I don't have to be guarded and constantly two steps ahead, strategizing how I'll react, is healing. Which leads me to repressed emotions, emotions that got stuffed so I wouldn't risk losing love. This is, after all, why humans repress emotions.

I grew up in a highly competitive, high performing family where vulnerability and emotions were frowned upon. I devoted a lot of pages to this experience.

But I don't blame my parents. They gave me exceptional opportunities to flourish and succeed, from learning a number of sports to earning advanced degrees. Expressing feelings wasn't encouraged though, which is not all that uncommon in families. Society hasn't exactly modeled how to fearlessly show our emotions to others without being criticized. It's not my parents' fault that they didn't foster an environment where I felt safe to convey my needs. They likely didn't get that from their parents, who didn't receive it from their parents and so on.

For a highly sensitive person like myself, squashing my true feelings did some damage.

I didn't learn how to process difficult and uncomfortable emotions; it seemed to me, the way to handle anything upsetting was to deal with it on my own, in private, so others wouldn't witness my pain. It was modeled to me that keeping up a good appearance in terms of keeping my feelings in check was more important than letting people see my sadness or anger—that's what I learned to do.

When I was little, I idealized my parents, like so many children do. I was Daddy's little girl and we had a good relationship. Those rose-colored glasses came off soon after developing arthritis, when I realized that not being the athlete who effortlessly excelled at all the sports did nothing in the way of earning points with him. Instead, I felt more pressure to measure up and more invisible because I was even farther behind.

My dad meant well, I could feel that, but his delivery lacked empathy, understanding, and warmth. I don't knock him for getting that wrong. The never-good-enough syndrome I developed is something he likely suffered from as well. I think when you're as good an athlete as my dad was or as successful as he was at his career, it sets you up for more confidence in other areas. Emotional intelligence, introspection, compassion: those weren't his strong points.

The comedian John Mulaney jokes about growing up with parents who were both lawyers. Apparently, he too, couldn't get away with much. Even when he was a child, his dad would speak to him as if he were on trial. He'd question him about his teeth brushing and practically make him weep. His mom would tell him the latest news and somehow implicate him in any reported crimes. That's precisely how my dad could make me feel, like I couldn't get away with anything; that he'd find the hole in any argument, and it was better to be on guard than at ease.

My mom sacrificed a lot of her dreams and desires to be with my dad. She would have preferred pursuing her acting career in New York City. She gave that up when he decided to run for office in Philadelphia. If I felt she wasn't emotionally available, it was likely a result of her upbringing, too. Unfortunately, I learned to cope with the sense that she wasn't there for me by shutting down.

Just because my parents couldn't verbalize their care, doesn't mean I doubted their love. They showed it in different ways.

I recognize that people who spew meanness are in a lot of emotional pain themselves. Their behavior toward others often has very little to do with the other person and a lot more to do with how they feel about themselves. Graham comes to mind.

As I said before, when Graham was healing the pain from his breakup in New York, he dabbled in therapy. He didn't stick with it very long; but at the time, he seemed interested in investigating some of our family history, exploring how our upbringing led him to be the person he is. He seemed nervous about digging too deeply, afraid of excavating too much, but he'll have to sort that out on his own, or not.

For all I know, Graham sees me with all the cloudiness that accompanies our relationship. He could very well assume that I got all the attention after I developed arthritis; after all, he was competing for the same limited quantity.

I often wonder whether I would have turned out like Graham had it not been for the arthritis. Would I have come across as condescending and insensitive as a byproduct of toughening up to prevent the sadness, hurt, and anger from overwhelming me?

Perhaps if he and my mom had a different relationship, we would have fared better as siblings and enjoyed each other's company. If we were closer, his golden boy status likely wouldn't have bothered me so much. There are a lot of variables that, had they been different, would have set my life on a much different path.

Experiencing distrust in my family, feeling unsafe to share my true feelings, feeling unnoticed, playing second fiddle to my brother, set me up to isolate, question who was really on my side, wonder where I stood with people, and develop difficulty discerning who accepted me for me. Perhaps, the only thing left to do is forgive them—my dad, my mom, Graham, and the rest—for being who they are, trapped human beings.

What I do know is that the way in which I came into the world, being a hypersensitive person combined with the dynamics of a family that didn't encourage expression of feelings and a perceived favoritism, set me up for going to extremes to be seen and heard—to feel as though I mattered. Had I not invented pain for myself, I'm certain I would have been like so many of my clients: I very likely would have developed pain or medically unexplained symptoms over the years as a result of repressing my feelings.

What I did do was craft a plan, one that I recognize now as an example of the nocebo effect (the opposite of the placebo effect), which describes believing so firmly in my conviction I would have visible pain in my body, that I created just that. But I did it to achieve an end result: unconditional love and attention. At age nine, I already saw the futility in that. I got what I wanted but it was ephemeral. Sympathy and special treatment expired but the arthritis didn't go away.

This condition made me search for answers because medications weren't cutting it. And I've long held the memory of how pain came into my life. I used to think that the arthritis would leave my body if I could just tap into the same manifesting abilities I used that created it. Yet ever since Apartment Boy, I've wondered if some other feeling or mental state needs to be experienced for healing to occur.

Now I know that for a reversal of symptoms to take

place I'll have to feel my way through the fear, learn to sit with vulnerability without running away, and allow the right people in. It's not just about intellectualizing and being able to understand my feelings from an analytical point of view but to really sink in and be enveloped in my experiences especially when things feel messy and uncomfortable.

Just like how I work with clients, the symptom is the entry way for unearthing the issues that need to come to the surface, be examined and allowed to be expressed. My issues of feeling like I wasn't enough when I was young, got buried deep into my subconscious under layers of other emotions. In order for a change to happen, I can't just think my way out of it.

I've watched how relationships, platonic and otherwise, have affected me. I've learned what issues seem to bypass my conscious brain and get stuck in my body. I've become better at recognizing emotions when I have them rather than letting my body absorb every feeling thrown its way like I used to. That's a big reason I believe I couldn't make the arthritis go away soon after I brought it into existence—I had to learn more about why I wanted pain in my body, what emotions were underneath crying out for attention I felt I wasn't getting.

Developing fatigue after 9/11 and recovering so quickly inspired me to learn how I could help other people heal, people who might feel defeated after hearing their doctor tell them nothing can offer them relief, nothing can make them better. I'm here to say that they don't have to just live with their pain or symptoms.

As I searched for my own answers, I continued to learn about how the mind and body are inextricably connected. My journey for relief landed me in this line of work. I've found methods that have helped, not just me, but my clients.

I see myself in my clients. I see the issues they bump up against. While the people I help become aware of their stories, I become aware of my own. As they open up to the understanding of how their experiences have shaped them, I understand the interplay in my own life. The people I help can accept the fact that their pain or symptom is a byproduct of their own patterns, of how they relate to themselves and to others. And so can I.

Those clients learned to repress their emotions; they didn't feel safe speaking up and expressing themselves without repercussions. As a result, they found themselves in physical pain. When I'm with my clients, I'm listening to and watching the family dynamics that played out for them. Some of their patterns were different than mine and some of them were remarkably similar.

Mind you, there are certainly many people whose pain is rooted in something else. Would they still feel better mentally and emotionally by looking at the thoughts and feelings they keep buried? Absolutely.

I can't help everyone, even if they present with these types of mind-body issues. Not everyone is ready to look deeply at the areas that are holding them back. For those people willing to look, relief is achieved on different timelines. Some get relief very quickly and others take longer to see results. That's because everyone is unique. We all come into this world with different fixed traits and personalities. We cope with people, events and emotions in our own specific ways. What I can do is shine the light on the junk buried in their subconscious. I've learned various techniques that allow me to be a conduit for clients to access parts of themselves they hadn't understood before. Ultimately, it's up to each client to heal. If the client decides nothing can make him or her well, there's nothing I (or anyone else) can do to help them.

If you recognize that you come from a background where it was easier to pretend that things were OK; if you were raised in a family where you felt unsafe revealing your needs and feelings; if you felt as though you had to deal with your issues on your own, then I encourage you to inquire about what you may have pushed out of conscious awareness. Because if you do, you might find that all those emotions need a voice. Once you give them space, you just might find relief from physical and emotional pain. Feeling, not repressing, is the golden ticket.

If you see yourself in my story or in the stories of my clients and recognize that you're a repressor who suffers from chronic physical pain or emotional ailments, you may well have issues connecting with yourself as well.

If you haven't benefited from traditional medicine or therapy; if you're still struggling to return to health and you've tried various paths that haven't alleviated your pain, your next step may be to look at your patterns of repressing emotions—to understand how they show up in your life, and examine how you relate to other people.

If you fell out of a tree and broke your leg or contracted a virus, perhaps these ideas may not apply. Then again, even an injury that presents as fully physical sometimes has a root and cure in the emotional realm. I've worked with enough professional athletes to see the truth in that.

I'm still on this healing mission. I sense that even when the arthritis is fully gone, my body will still speak to me in symptoms to alert me to danger. I don't always consciously recognize when something or someone feels off, but my body sure does. My job, and perhaps yours, is all about connecting to myself and to others in an authentic way, to stop obfus-cating because I'm afraid to get hurt.

I'm acutely aware that I don't trust other people easily. I know that I avoid vulnerability, particularly in romantic relationships, because I'm worried that others will use that perceived weakness against me. I assume that most people are not warm and emotionally safe, and all of these fears have blocked connection and love for me.

How then do we find love and connection?

I've learned it starts by looking back at all the ways our feelings felt so paralyzing that we repressed them. My job is to help my clients identify the emotions that are connected to past events that had feelings associated with them that were never fully processed. Some clients are so tired of the pain they're willing to take a closer look at those difficult percep-tions and outcomes. Some people aren't ready.

Here's what comes next . . .

What would happen if you (and I) were to tell the truth? Tell the person or persons with whom you most want to con-nect that you're scared to reveal your true feelings, that vul-nerability terrifies you, that asking for reciprocity is not your expertise? What would happen if you got real and expressed all the parts of yourself that you think are unattractive? More importantly, how might you react if the person hearing all this empathized with you, told you he or she (or they) not only got it but appreciated you sharing those things, and felt even closer to you and loved you even more for expressing them?

When people are authentic, when they let their tags show and don't try to cover up their true feelings, it allows an opening for closeness and deeper love to develop.

The idea that your needs can be met by another person,

that you can trust and depend on others without the overwhelming fear of rejection is scary (trust me, I know), but it's what produces healing of physical and emotional pain. It's been the case for me, and I've seen it take shape for my clients.

When we tell the truth, show who we truly are, including our messy feelings, and we're accepted, that's what catalyzes healing.

Humans don't exist in individual pods never interacting with anyone else around them. We're social beings. It's no wonder that solitary confinement is used as a form of punishment and torture. We need human interaction and we require love and support to flourish. The lack of it weakens and its abundance fortifies.

Do I still believe that love is the ingredient that will heal pain? Yes.

Perhaps you do, too.

WANT MORE?

When experiencing emotional trauma, depression, anxiety, or chronic pain, the first response is often to seek conventional treatment, such as medication. But what do you do when you've exhausted the traditional routes, and you're still in physical and emotional pain—how do you find the relief you're seeking?

You can visit me at www.drserenasterling.com for more information.

Or you can download my free report, *How to Get Out of Pain Fast: 3 Secrets Most Doctors Won't Tell You,* by going to https://drserenasterling.com/how-to-get-out-pain-fast/.

ACKNOWLEDGEMENTS

First and foremost, I want to thank my clients who have shared their lives with me and entrusted me to help them on their healing journey. Their courage to look within, uncover their wounds, and show up differently makes me incredibly grateful to be of service.

Ever since earning a master's in international journalism, I've wanted to write a book. I had some ideas swirling through my mind a few years ago but kept deciding it wasn't time for one reason or another. On my first day at an in-depth, four-month course on public speaking, Michael Port asked me and my fellow classmates why we were playing small and why we were keeping our stories to ourselves, the ones that could change other people's lives. Unbeknownst to him, I decided that day that I would dive in, write this book, and finally tell my story.

Thanks goes to my friend, Julie Horns, who I met in my second year of grad school for psychology, for talking through some ideas and concepts I had for this book.

I'm grateful to my friend, Jodee Winter, my first true friend in Seattle, for getting me out of the house and keeping me balanced while I worked and wrote. She made sure I had fun.

I can't believe I've been friends with Ryan Sager since 2000. "Is this what we're going to be saying in another twenty years?" He always knows how to make me laugh. I'm grateful for his help in pulling looks together for my professional photos. His eye for style keeps me feeling young.

Who knew that Craigslist.org, back in 2010, would come through with such a stellar graphic designer as Simon Bucktrout? After he created my first logo and business cards, I remember being so stoked I considered all the products on which I could put the logo: stationary, t-shirts, my duvet cover! When it came time to consider my book cover, I knew Simon was the perfect person to execute the job and I'm so pleased with his product.

I appreciate the help of my copy editor, Amy Brueggeman, and proofreader, Janet Ivaldi, who caught grammatical mistakes and asked just the right questions in order to make this book read as well as it does.

I'm so thankful to this publishing house, Summit Press, for taking a chance on me, especially with me being a first-time author.

Thank you also goes to Ana Melikian, my business coach at the time I considered endeavoring to write this book, who enthusiastically congratulated me for doing so. Ana is responsible for referring me to Ann Sheybani, my book coach.

If it weren't for Ann, I'm certain this book would be a stack of loose-leaf papers shelved somewhere in the furthermost corner of my closet. Beyond holding me accountable to meeting deadlines, delving deeper into stories, and unearthing the important details, she brought out my courage, which had laid dormant for way too many years. Together, we brought this book to light.

ABOUT THE AUTHOR

SERENA STERLING HAS AN MA in International Journalism from City University in London, England, and a PsyD in clinical psychology from the California Institute of Integral Studies in San Francisco and is a certified life coach. She sees people from all over the world remotely and specializes in working with people with chronic pain and medically unexplained symptoms. You can reach her at serena@drserenasterling.com

Made in the USA
Monee, IL
28 May 2021

68770573R00148